THE STATE OF THE
ENVIRONMENT

THE STATE OF THE MARINE ENVIRONMENT

GESAMP

(IMO/FAO/UNESCO/WMO/WHO/IAEA/UN/UNEP
Joint Group of Experts on the Scientific Aspects
of Marine Pollution)

OXFORD

BLACKWELL SCIENTIFIC PUBLICATIONS

LONDON EDINBURGH BOSTON

MELBOURNE PARIS BERLIN VIENNA

Blackwell Scientific Publications
Editorial Offices:
Osney Mead, Oxford OX2 0EL
25 John Street, London WC1N 2BL
23 Ainslie Place, Edinburgh EH3 6AJ
3 Cambridge Center, Cambridge,
    Massachusetts 02142, USA
54 University Street, Carlton
    Victoria 3053, Australia

Other Editorial Offices:
Arnette SA
2, rue Casimir-Delavigne
75006 Paris
France

Blackwell Wissenschaft
Meinekestrasse 4
D-1000 Berlin 15
Germany

Blackwell MZV
Feldgasse 13
A-1238 Wien
Austria

First published 1990 in Nairobi, Kenya by
    IMO/FAO/UNESCO/WMO/WHO/ IAEA/UN/
    UNEP Joint Group of Experts on the Scientific
    Aspects of Marine Pollution (GESAMP): under
    the title The state of the marine environment.
    Rep. Stud. GESAMP No. 39. 111 pp.
Also issued by UNEP as UNEP Regional Seas
    Reports and Studies No. 115.
This edition published 1991 by Blackwell
    Scientific Publications

Set by Best-set Typesetter Ltd, Hong Kong
Printed and bound in Great Britain by
Hartnolls Ltd, Bodmin, Cornwall.

DISTRIBUTORS

Marston Book Services Ltd
PO Box 87
Oxford OX2 0DT
(*Orders*: Tel: 0865 791155
        Fax: 0865 791927
        Telex: 837515)

USA
    Blackwell Scientific Publications, Inc.
    3 Cambridge Center
    Cambridge MA 02142
    (*Orders*: Tel: 800 759-6102)

Canada
    Oxford University Press
    70 Wynford Drive
    Don Mills
    Ontario M3C 1J9
    (*Orders*: Tel: 416 441-2941)

Australia
    Blackwell Scientific Publications
    (Australia) Pty Ltd
    54 University Street
    Carlton, Victoria 3053
    (*Orders*: Tel: 03 347-0300)

British Library
Cataloguing in Publication Data
GESAMP
    The state of the marine environment.
    1. Oceans. Pollution
    I. Title
    363.7394

ISBN 0-632-03198-0

Library of Congress
Cataloging in Publication Data
The State of the marine environment / GESAMP
    (IMO/FAO/UNESCO/WMO/WHO/IAEA/UN/
    UNEP Joint Group of Experts on the Scientific
    Aspects of Marine Pollution).
        p.   cm.
    Includes bibliographical references and index.
    ISBN 0-632-03198-0
    1. Marine pollution.   I. IMO/FAO/
    UNESCO/WMO/WHO/IAEA/UN/UNEP
    Joint Group of Experts on the Scientific Aspects
    of Marine Pollution.
    GC1085.S73   1991
    363.73'94'09162—dc20   91-6432
                                                CIP

GESAMP is an advisory body consisting of specialized experts nominated by the Sponsoring Agencies (International Maritime Organization, Food and Agriculture Organization of the United Nations, United Nations Educational, Scientific and Cultural Organization, World Meteorological Organization, World Health Organization, International Atomic Energy Agency, United Nations, United Nations Environment Programme). Its principal task is to provide scientific advice on marine pollution problems to the Sponsoring Agencies and to the Intergovernmental Oceanographic Commission (IOC).

This book contains views expressed by members of GESAMP who act in their individual capacities; their views may not necessarily correspond with those of the Sponsoring Agencies.

Contents

Preface

DEFINITION OF MARINE POLLUTION

Pollution means the introduction by man, directly or indirectly, of substances or energy into the marine environment (including estuaries) resulting in such deleterious effects as harm to living resources, hindrance to marine activities including fishing, impairment of quality for use of seawater and reduction of amenities.

GESAMP is an international group of experts sponsored by the United Nations to assess current and future threats to the marine environment. They look at the effects of chemical pollution (including oil, heavy metals, chlorinated hydrocarbons and radioactivity) and describe the consequences of increasing exploitation of the coast due to population growth, accelerating urbanization, greater affluence and faster transport.

This book contains their analysis of the effects which these forms of pollution have had upon the oceans and sets out their proposals for immediate action.

Although the idea of summarizing the state of marine pollution in the world oceans is probably much older than one might imagine, the specific idea of reviewing the health of the oceans seems to have first arisen in the report of the ACMRR/SCOR/WMO Joint Working Party on Global Ocean Research (Ponza and Rome, 29 April–7 May 1969).

This idea was taken up by the ACMRR/SCOR/ACOMR/GESAMP Joint Working Party on the Global Investigation of Pollution in the Marine Environment (San Marco de Castellabate and Rome, 11–18 October 1971).

The Action Plan adopted at the United Nations Conference on the Human Environment (Stockholm, 5–16 June 1972) recommended that GESAMP should assemble scientific data and provide advice on scientific aspects of marine pollution especially those of an interdisciplinary nature.

The IOC International Co-ordination Group for GIPME at its first session (London, 2–6 April 1973) recommended that IOC retain a consultant to bring together the available data into a report on the Health of the Oceans. Professor E. D. Goldberg was asked to do this work, and his report was published by UNESCO in 1976.[1]

The fifteenth session of the Inter-Secretariat Committee on Scientific Programmes Relating to Oceanography (ICSPRO), recommended 'that GESAMP should be invited to advise agencies, and UNEP was asked to take the initiative, in consultation with other agencies, for the preparation of a detailed request to GESAMP for a critical examination of present and planned methods by which to generate a continuous authoritative review and assessment of the health of the oceans.' The initiative requested of UNEP was taken up at the meeting of the GESAMP Joint Secretariat (Geneva, 4–5 June 1977) when it was decided that the preparation of 'periodic reviews of the state of the marine environment as regards marine pollution' should become one of the main terms of reference for GESAMP.[2]

The first review on the state of the marine environment was completed by GESAMP under the co-ordination of Professor Gunnar Kullenberg and was published by UNESCO and UNEP in 1982.[3]

The preparation of the second review on the state of the marine environment through GESAMP was initiated by UNEP in 1985. A Working Group (Appendix A) was established under the chairmanship of Professor Alasdair McIntyre to prepare the report under the overall guidance of GESAMP. The present book is the report; as endorsed by the 19th session of GESAMP (Athens, 8–12 May 1989, Appendix B).

The book is based on 16 technical annexes (Appendix C) written by individual experts commissioned by the Chairman of the Working Group. While GESAMP takes responsibility for the

[1] Goldberg, E. D. (1976) The Health of the Oceans UNESCO, Paris.

[2] The Joint Group of Experts on the Scientific Aspects of Marine Pollution (GESAMP) is an advisory body to the Heads of eight organizations of the United Nations System (UN, UNEP, FAO, UNESCO, WHO, WMO, IMO and IAEA).

[3] Rep. Stnd. GESAMP (15) and UNEP Regional Seas Reports and Studies No. 16.

substance of the report, the annexes were endorsed by the Working Group, but are the responsibility of their individual authors. The technical annexes have been published by UNEP as a separate publication.

In addition to drawing on technical annexes and on other GESAMP reports (Appendix D), this book is also based on information culled from the open literature (Appendix E).

The Working Group was assisted in its task by the parallel but independent work of 12 UNEP-sponsored Task Teams which will result in the publication of 12 regional reviews on the state of the marine environment, written largely according to the layout of this report. The regional reviews are being published by UNEP.

The organizations sponsoring GESAMP would like to acknowledge with appreciation the work of the drafting group (Dr Gwyneth Howells, Professor Alasdair McIntyre and Dr Francesco Sella) for their role in preparing the final version of this report.

List of Abbreviations

CCCO	Committee on Climate Change and the Ocean
CFC	Chlorofluorocarbons
DDE	1, 1-dichloro-2, 2-bis (p-chlorophenyl) ethylene
DDT	1, 1, 1-trichloro-2, 2-bis (p-chlorophenyl) ethylene
DSP	Diarrhoeic shellfish poisoning
EC	Environmental capacity
EQO	Environmental quality objective
FAO	Food and Agriculture Organization
GEEP	Group of Experts on Environmental Pollutants
GESAMP	Group of Experts on the Scientific Aspects of Marine Pollution
grt	Gross registered tons
Gt	Gigatonne
HCB	Hexachlorobenzene
HCH	Hexachlorohexane
IAEA	International Atomic Energy Agency
ICES	International Council for the Exploration of the Sea
ICRP	International Commission for Radiological Protection
IMDG	International Maritime Dangerous Goods Code
IMO	International Maritime Organization
IOC	International Oceanographic Commission
JGOFS	Joint Global Ocean Flux Study
LDC	London Dumping Convention
MARPOL	International Convention for the Prevention of Pollution from Ships
mSv	Millisievert
Mt	Megatonne
OILPOL	International Convention for the Prevention of Pollution of the Sea by Oil
OTEC	Ocean thermal energy conversion
PAH	Polyaromatic hydrocarbons

xii *List of Abbreviations*

PBq	Petabecquerel
PCB	Polychlorinated biphenyls
ppb	parts per billion
ppm	parts per million
ppmv	parts per million per volume
PSP	Paralytic shellfish poisoning
TBT	Tributyltin
TOGA	Tropical Ocean and Global Atmosphere Programme
UES	Uniform Emission Standard
UN	United Nations
UNEP	United Nations Environment Programme
UNESCO	United Nations Educational Scientific and Cultural Organization
UNSCEAR	United Nations Committee on the Effects of Atomic Radiation
UV	Ultraviolet
WCRP	World Climate Research Programme
WHO	World Health Organization
WMO	World Meteorological Organization
WOCE	World Ocean Circulation Experiment

Summary

- Today man's fingerprint is found everywhere in the oceans. Chemical contamination and litter can be observed from the poles to the tropics and from beaches to abyssal depths. But conditions in the marine environment vary widely.

- The open sea is still relatively clean. Low levels of lead, synthetic organic compounds and artificial radionuclides, though widely detectable, are biologically insignificant. Oil slicks and litter are common along sea lanes, but are, at present, of minor consequence to communities of organisms living in open-ocean waters.

- In contrast to the open ocean, the margins of the sea are affected by man almost everywhere, and encroachment on coastal areas continues worldwide. Habitats are being lost irretrievably to the construction of harbours and industrial installations, to the development of tourist facilities and mariculture, and to the growth of settlements and cities. Although difficult to quantify, destruction of beaches, coral reefs and wetlands, including mangrove forests, as well as increasing erosion of the shore, are evident all over the world. If unchecked, this trend will lead to global deterioration in the quality and productivity of the marine environment.

- The growing exploitation of the coast is a reflection of population increase, accelerating urbanization, greater affluence and faster transport – trends that will continue throughout the world. Controlling coastal development and protecting habitats will require changes in planning both inland and on the coast, often involving painful social and political choices.

- A wide range of activities on land contributes to the release of contaminants to the sea either directly or carried by rivers and the atmosphere, while sea-borne activities make a minor addition. Only a small part of those contaminants has spread beyond the limits of the continental shelf. The bulk remains in coastal waters and, in places, particularly in poorly flushed areas, has built up to significant levels. Our views on these contaminants are summarized below in what is judged as their current order of importance.

- The rate of introduction of nutrients, chiefly nitrates but sometimes also phosphates, is increasing, and areas of eutrophication are expanding, along with enhanced frequency and scale of unusual plankton blooms and excessive seaweed growth. The two major sources of nutrients to coastal waters are sewage disposal and agricultural run-off from fertilizer-treated fields and from intensive stock raising. The degree of damage varies from area to area, reflecting site conditions and nutrient load. Nutrient contamination is costly in terms of lost resources and spoiled amenity but effective remedial action is difficult. It will involve large investments in treatment plants and in sludge and effluent disposal, and major changes in agricultural practices. It is also difficult to relate these inputs to the occurrence of blooms because the quantitative relations between nutrient input and eutrophication are unclear and because of the confounding role of other ecological factors and of climatic variations.

- Microbial contamination from sewage causes many human diseases, including cholera and hepatitis A. Control requires proper design and siting of outfalls, coupled with rigorous surveillance of shellfish beds and their marketed products, and the timely banning of contaminated seafood. Microbial contamination of sea water is also responsible for widespread outbreaks of gastro-intestinal diseases at ill-protected and crowded beaches and is a suspected cause of respiratory, ear and skin infections among bathers.

- The haphazard disposal of plastic material on land and from ships results in littering of beaches and seriously damages marine wildlife, particularly sea mammals, diving birds and reptiles. These may be injured by the ingestion of plastic fragments, or entrapped in plastic packing and fishing gear. Enforcement of existing regulations on land and at sea, and increased public education, should reduce considerably the amount of plastic refuse, while better design and utilization of plastics for packing and fishing purposes would minimize the risk to marine organisms.

- Among synthetic organic compounds of concern, chlorinated hydrocarbons, though still high in the sediments of industrial coastal areas and in fatty tissue of top predators such as seals, are now decreasing in some northern temperate areas where restrictions on their use have been enforced long enough. Current levels have not caused widespread harm to marine life so far, with the exception of impaired reproduction in some mammals and fish-eating birds. Contamination appears to be rising in tropical and sub-tropical areas owing to the continued use of chlorinated pesticides there. Because chlorinated hydrocarbons persist in sediments, from which they may be reintroduced to the wider ecosystem, monitoring of organisms and sediments should continue. Recent recognition of the toxicity of the anti-fouling agent tributyltin for a number of species has resulted in early action to control its use in a few countries, and this control should be extended.

- Oil is a highly visible contaminant. Notwithstanding the impact of large accidental spills, its main global impact is due to tar balls which, although generally harmless to marine organisms, may foul beaches and interfere with recreational activities, sometimes with major economic consequences in tourist areas. The presence of petroleum hydrocarbons in sea water and particularly in sediments, however, continues to be a matter of concern locally after accidents have released large amounts of oil that accumulate in sheltered areas, affecting amenity and living resources, especially bird life. While the damage is not irreversible, recovery can be slow.

- Trace elements such as cadmium, lead and mercury, which occur in the marine environment both naturally and as a result of human activities, are now of less concern, except where high levels occur near contamination sources. Their discharge, however, should be kept under surveillance and monitoring should be continued to ensure compliance with current acceptable limits.

- Radioactive contamination generates widespread public fears. Although artificial radionuclides from a number of sources, including nuclear installations, fall-out from weapon testing and, more recently, from the accident at Chernobyl, have added to the levels naturally occurring in sea water, these additions have had insignificant effects on man and other organisms. Planned discharges of radioactive effluents (e.g.

from reprocessing plants) are tightly regulated and monitored, and the amounts currently released are decreasing.

- While attention is focussed mainly on contaminants that are clearly detectable in the sea, there is concern that very low concentrations of toxic substances may produce effects at the sublethal level that could build up over long periods with significant damage to ecosystems. It is recommended that the special studies required to address this problem be encouraged.

- The global yield of fisheries has continued to increase in the past decade partly by exploitation of new stocks, but a combination of overfishing and stock fluctuations due to natural events has led to the decline of certain fisheries and to instability of others. Toxic and microbial agents have not so far affected exploitable living resources on a wide scale, although some stocks, especially of shellfish in limited areas, have been declared unfit for human consumption. However, coastal nursery grounds and shallow waters are being increasingly degraded, and marine resources, both wild and farmed, could eventually be damaged on a global scale. In addition, the exploitation of living marine resources may degrade the environment by damaging habitats and altering food webs, while mariculture, which is rapidly expanding, generates its own local pollution and may upset the ecological balance by the introduction of exotic species and diseases.

- These are problems on which action can be identified now. There are additional issues that cannot at present be fully assessed in relation to the seas, namely, the effects of climate change, including a possible rise in sea level resulting from global warming due to increases in greenhouse gases, and the impact of a reduction of stratospheric ozone, which may affect marine resources through increased exposure to ultraviolet radiation.

- A number of international agreements now supplement national regulations aimed at protecting the seas. They concern mainly pollution from sea-borne sources and have played a role in reducing ocean pollution, particularly by oil residues. However, much remains to be done to control land-based sources, the main contributors to contamination of the sea.

- We conclude that, at the start of the 1990s, the major causes of immediate concern in the marine environment on a global basis are coastal development and the attendant destruction of habitats, eutrophication, microbial contamination of seafood and beaches, fouling of the seas by plastic litter, progressive build-up of chlorinated hydrocarbons, especially in the tropics and the sub-tropics, and accumulation of tar on beaches. However, concerns may differ from region to region, reflecting local situations and priorities. Furthermore, throughout the world, public perception may still accord greater importance to other contaminants such as radionuclides, trace elements and oil. These were highlighted in the 1982 GESAMP Review and are considered again in the present book, but we now regard them as being of lesser concern.

- While no areas of the ocean and none of its principal resources appear to be irrevocably damaged, and most are still unpolluted, while there are encouraging signs that in some areas marine contamination is decreasing, we are concerned that too little is being done to correct or anticipate situations that call for action, that not enough consideration is being given to the consequences for the oceans of coastal development, and that activities on land continue with little regard to their effects in coastal waters. We fear, especially in view of the continuing growth of human populations, that the marine environment could deteriorate significantly in the next decade unless strong, co-ordinated national and international action is taken now. At the national level in particular, the concerted application of measures to reduce wastes and to conserve raw materials will be essential. The efforts will be great and the costs high, but nothing less will ensure the continued health of the sea and the maintenance of its resources.

Introduction

Aims and Coverage of the Review

The need to ensure the wholesome condition of the oceans is now generally recognized. As we move into the 1990s it may seem that a reassuring index of the health of the marine environment is provided by the most recent fisheries information from the UN Food and Agriculture Organization, showing that the annual global catch rose in 1987 to a new record of 92.7 million tonnes, with a confident forecast that 100 million tonnes will be reached before the end of the century. However, this yield is attained against the background of overstressed stocks, increasing fishing effort, and a switching to less desirable species, as well as a deterioration of inshore nursery grounds.

Semi-enclosed areas are increasingly showing signs of pollution, raising the question of whether all coastal zones, including well-flushed areas, will become damaged to the same degree, and whether eventually even the open ocean will be affected. An adequate assessment of the present state of the marine environment must take into account all the pressures on the world's seas, the changes in our understanding of marine ecology and pollution, and the new attitudes to environmental quality that are emerging.

While acknowledging that marine pollution arises from the actions of man, it is becoming clear that it cannot be attributed solely to activities performed directly in the oceans. This book, then, begins by identifying and discussing the main human activities that affect the marine environment. These involve a diversity of operations along the coastline, as well as the manipulation of the hydrological cycle and various land-use practices often carried out far inland; they include offshore activities such as waste disposal and marine transportation, and also the exploitation of marine resources, living and non-living.

Since these activities are often associated with the production of chemical wastes, the review goes on to examine the concentration and distribution of chemical contaminants in the sea. The validity of many earlier measurements is questioned, and the difficulties of obtaining reliable data that can be used to detect changes and recognize long-term trends in time and space are highlighted. The general inadequacy of the data base is emphasized, in particular the paucity of information for the open ocean and for inshore areas in some parts of the world. The significance of the observed contaminant levels is discussed, and special attention is paid to a number of substances of common concern at present, including synthetic biocides, radioactive materials and oil residues.

The biological impact of man's activities is considered, particularly the effects of wastewater discharges on human health, and the changes of inshore ecosystems caused by nutrient inputs. The increasing loss of natural coastal habitats around the world is documented, with special reference to wetlands such as mangrove forests, to seagrass beds and to the very sensitive coral ecosystems. Longer-term problems include the possibility of subtle effects of persistent low levels of contamination, as well as the effects of an increased ultraviolet flux due to depletion of the stratospheric ozone layer, and the consequences of increases in the 'greenhouse' gases which are expected to produce a rise in sea level and a change in climate patterns with unknown effects on marine ecosystems.

The increasing world population, its preferential settlement in the coastal zone and the resulting industrialization of that area will only exacerbate the problems at the margins of the seas, in contrast to the open oceans. These problems arise at a time of increasing environmental awareness, and it is important that a broad and balanced view be taken of how best to protect the environment. The essential linkage between terrestrial, aquatic and marine compartments should be recognized, and all available options considered.

At the same time it is important to distinguish between perceived and real problems, recognizing that the assessment of an issue by the scientific community may differ from that of the general public. While public perceptions, however unsubstantial, must be taken seriously, and while it is entirely proper that political action should take account of them, efforts should be made to provide rational explanations and ensure that the public is well informed about the state of the current knowledge. It should also be recognized that what is possible and indeed mandatory for an industrialized country may need to be viewed in a different light in the developing world.

Against this background, the book considers the existing mechanisms for protecting the marine environment and controlling pollution. It refers to their national and international aspects and concludes with an overview of the most important problems facing the seas.

Almost ten years have now passed since GESAMP presented its first report on the health of the oceans in 1982. It is relevant to note briefly some of the changes that have taken place in that decade. Analytical techniques have been improved, satellite observations have come into use for large-scale studies, techniques for process control and pollution abatement have been further developed, new national legislation and regulations have been introduced, and international agreements reached on a wide range of environmental issues. Significant changes have occurred in the pattern of energy use, with associated reductions in the amount of oil transported at sea. Finally, there have been some major accidents involving shipping, the chemical industry and nuclear installations. The scientific literature on marine pollution has increased by at least 50%. A greater degree of public interest and sensitivity to the environment has developed, raising expectations and causing changes in priorities for action. These are reflected in the discussions that follow.

The purpose of the book is to document and assess the current state of the marine environment, and to identify the major global concerns and priorities for action in both the short and the medium term. Longer-term issues associated with increases in levels of atmospheric CO_2 and other greenhouse gases are being dealt with by a number of other international groups and are only briefly reviewed here.

While primarily addressed to the Executive Heads of the organizations that support GESAMP, the book also aims at providing a balanced assessment of the state of the marine environment for other national and international policy-makers, and for the concerned lay public in general.

Chapter 1

Human Activities Affecting the Sea

In discussing the state of the oceans it is appropriate to focus on those human activities that are likely to affect the marine environment. This chapter examines the most important of them. For some the impact is a matter of immediate concern, particularly where human health is involved, and prompt action is required. For others, there will be consequences only in the medium or long term, but it is none the less important to recognize problems as early as possible so that effective measures can be initiated before damage occurs.

1.1 Development of Coastal Areas

The coastline is a complex region comprising bays, estuaries and large semi-enclosed areas where human populations and industrial development are concentrated. It is the focus for contaminants from inland areas as well as from developments along its length. Most of the sources of contamination discussed in this chapter contribute directly or indirectly to problems in the immediate coastal zone, and arise from activities specifically located there.

Although a relationship between human population increase and environmental change has long been recognized, attempts have been made only recently to assess the cumulative impacts of land development in the coastal zone by recording their physical, chemical and biological consequences. This requires knowledge of trends in water quality and an understanding of the management of aquatic habitats. Equally important is the economic analysis of damage to natural resources and human health against which the cost of control measures will need to be justified. Many of the impacts recorded are common to most coastal developments, but it is useful to consider industrial and recreational activities separately.

The development and maintenance of ports and harbours is of prime concern to human populations. Water exchange in these areas is often limited and shipping activities introduce contaminants, including oily wastes, cargo escapement and human wastes released from shipboard. These are subject to national and international regulations, but contamination at ports is difficult to control since it enters the sea by many routes, including discharges from pipes, run-off from streets, roofs and parking areas, and inputs from the atmosphere. Also, harbours are the first point of contact with the sea for many rivers, which add a wide variety and large quantity of land-derived material.

In addition to the activities within the harbour itself, all large ports are provided with a wide range of services and support facilities, including roads, railways, shipyards, power plants and local waste disposal sites, each of which add to the general contamination. Their collective effects may be well recognized but are poorly studied.

After release or discharge to the sea, many contaminants become associated with sediments and may remain sequestered until resuspended by waves and currents or until the sediments are disturbed by dredging to maintain shipping channels. This dredging not only stirs up contaminated material and reintroduces it into the water column, it also brings the problem of dredge spoil disposal, and may give rise to changed patterns of water circulation. In general, harbour sediments carry particularly large chemical contaminant loads, significantly greater than in adjacent areas. Fish or shellfish harvested from these locations are usually tainted by petroleum, which affects their flavour adversely, and levels of contaminants in edible tissues may be high, and fail to meet health standards.

The recreational use of coastal waters for various leisure activities such as bathing, diving, boating and fishing is increasing. In some areas this represents the major, or even the only, industry. With the world-wide pressure to open up new locations for tourist development, pristine wetlands and swamps are being developed as recreational beaches and harbours for small vessels, or as sites for commercial and domestic activity. As well as structural engineering alterations to beaches themselves, the immediate hinterland is built up with hotels and support infrastructure. The resulting restructuring along the coastline disrupts traditional fisheries, interferes with marine life and eliminates important habitats. Ironically, this environmental degradation and congestion may destroy the main natural assets on which the tourism development is based.

An intrinsic feature of such developments is the influx of large numbers of people, at least seasonally, resulting in an increase of sewage outflow such that locally available means of treatment and disposal may be overtaxed. There is also increased traffic and general disturbance from activity, noise and lights, which many users expect and accept even in areas where damage will be caused. Not surprisingly, inhabitants of coastal areas identified for development often support schemes that they see as enhancing their income and standard of living. Local authorities and national governments also tend to encourage the influx of foreign currency.

The widespread consequences of all these developments are increasingly recognized. As a result, areas of high sensitivity or of special interest are being designated for protection through zoning and planning procedures, and species particularly at risk, such as many birds which feed or nest in wetlands, and sea turtles which lay eggs at the high water mark of sandy beaches, are being included in protocols for legal protection. Much more, however, remains to be done to reconcile conflicting demands when major alterations of the coastal strip are envisaged.

Indeed, planning of the development of the coastline as a whole, already being done in a number of countries, should be undertaken more widely. International guidelines, including criteria and standards, would provide valuable assistance in such planning in different geographical areas, but awareness, resources and political will are needed if the health of the resident and the transient populations, the survival of marine wildlife and the functional integrity of the vital land/sea interface are to be maintained.

1.2   Discharge of Wastewaters

Contaminants from land reach the marine environment by a variety of pathways. Coastal outfalls discharge directly to estuaries, inshore waters, bays and open coastal areas. Storm-water flows may be too great for drainage and treatment facilities and, when run-off is too fast, may exceed the assimilative capacity of the receiving waters. Rivers act as large-scale collectors and carriers of wastewaters from diverse sources within their drainage basins and offload them to the sea. Thus, rivers can be regarded as major point sources of mixed contaminants, the inputs of which depend on the contaminant load of the rivers and on the physico-chemical and biological transformations taking place in the river itself, and especially in the estuaries and the near-shore zone.

Non-point sources draining to coastal waters include surface run-off from agricultural areas, wash-out of agrochemicals and transport of sediment due to coastal erosion or to deforestation and desertification in the hinterland. Land management practices largely determine these various influxes.

River inputs and non-point sources are discussed elsewhere (Section 2.1). This chapter focusses on direct discharges from point sources along the coastline. Two are predominant: domestic sewage and industrial effluents. In urban areas both waste streams are often mixed in sewerage systems and reach the sea together as municipal wastewater. This then contains material of domestic origin as well as a variety of industrial and other effluents with higher concentrations of contaminants which have been discharged to the community sewerage systems.

Contaminants from these sources can be grouped as follows:

- micro-organisms
- organic material affecting oxygen balance
- nutrients
- trace elements
- synthetic organic compounds
- petroleum-related compounds
- particulates/sediments
- heat

It should be emphasized that effluents usually contain a mixture of these, the composition varying in both the short and the long term.

A specific agent or compound within any of these classes can exert varying degrees of impact on the marine environment. The magnitude of this impact is a function of the chemical and biological characteristics of the compound, its form, total amount and concentration, persistence, bioaccumulation, recycling potential and of the characteristics of the receiving environment. The early identification of substances that may have adverse effects on human health, living resources and the marine ecosystem is particularly important. The possibility of synergistic action of substances in a mixed discharge must be taken into account, although evidence so far suggests that synergism is unusual, and that an assumption of additive effects is usually realistic.

Wastewater discharges at the coast affect all compartments of the marine environment and may interefere with human uses. The most widespread effects of urban and industrial discharges are:

- health risks from the presence of sewage pathogens
- eutrophication and/or oxygen depletion due to nutrients and organic carbon
- toxic effects on marine organisms or risk to human health caused by various chemicals in seafood.

In addition, both eutrophication and toxic effects on marine organisms can damage marine living resources.

Many human pathogens, once released to coastal waters, die rapidly owing to adverse conditions in the marine environment. They may, however, be taken up by filter-feeding shellfish and some are able to proliferate in an intermediate host organism. The health consequences of consuming uncooked contaminated shellfish and of bathing in waters containing faecal micro-organisms are further discussed in Section 3.1.

Noticeable algal blooms in coastal waters are often an early sign of excessive nutrient inputs, and their decay adds to the problem of the oxygen demand due to organic materials from domestic sewage, livestock wastes and various agro-industries (e.g. pulp and paper mills, fish and food processing, sugar refineries). Effects are most severe where the effluents from densely populated industrial areas discharge to semi-enclosed or shallow receiving waters with reduced circulation, long residence times and hence limited scope for self-cleansing.

Major sources of industrial chemical discharges are pulp and paper mills, iron and steelworks, petroleum refineries, petrochemical industries, fertilizer factories, leather tanning and finishing, and other chemistry-based production installations, including pharmaceutical plants. These discharges are complex and, without appropriate treatment and properly sited outfalls, may be harmful to a variety of marine targets and, indirectly, to man. Localized fish kills (e.g. in fish farms), altered benthic communities, and accumulated chemical residues, are often the first warning of chemical pollution.

In the past, most pollution control strategies had been prompted, usually *post hoc*, by evident effects of, for example, excessive oxygen demand, or of discharge of nutrients, metals and pathogenic organisms, but recent and current policies try to forestall effects by controlling inputs, defining potentially hazardous substances and stringently limiting their disposal. However, toxicological information by itself cannot be the basis of control. Knowledge of discharge loading and dilution rates, as well as evidence of effects on specific organisms, is required.

Few municipal wastewater treatment plants handle domestic sewage alone; most have an industrially contributed load in addition, restricting the options for efficient waste treatment and sludge utilization. The degree of contaminant removal and the nature of the effluent discharge depend upon the types of substances released from industry, the treatment process technology used, the design of the treatment plant and its operational efficiency. Most of the large urban/industrial centres in developing countries have no effective wastewater treatment system, and the siting and design of their outfalls often do not provide adequate dilution and dispersion, thus potentially endangering human health and resources.

Even in developed countries, large population centres are still likely sources of contaminants through their untreated domestic effluents. Thus, while Marseilles, France, has very recently set up a modern sewage treatment plant, a number of large cities on the industrialized northern shore of the Mediterranean and its hinterland still lack one. Even when facilities are available, they may be inadequate when load is high owing to seasonal increases. In these cases additional treatment for peak load capacity can be costly to provide, and overflow release may be preferred in the short term, but appropriately sited offshore outfalls are needed, and these require surveillance to ensure that they are, and continue to be, effective.

In tropical and sub-tropical oceanic areas where long stretches of the coast may be rather sparsely populated, most of the sewage from small communities either does not reach the sea or is too diluted on discharge to cause detectable harm. Notable exceptions are population centres in coastal areas and estuaries in Latin/Central America, South-East Asia and Western Africa and some small but densely populated oceanic islands. During storms, domestic and industrial wastewaters from large metropolitan areas often reach the sea through storm-water overflow and open canals, receiving no treatment. Seafood harvested in these places constitutes one of the major public health hazards related to the marine environment.

1.3 Disposal of Dredged Material, Industrial Wastes and Sewage Sludges

1.3.1 Dredged material and mine tailings

About 80 to 90% of all material dumped at sea results from dredging. Between 1980 and 1985 the reports provided to the Secretariat of the London Dumping Convention (LDC) record an average of 215 million tonnes of dredged material dumped at sea annually, which represents some 20–22% of all dredged material, the rest being disposed of elsewhere. Of the total material dredged, about two-thirds are associated with operations to keep harbours, rivers and other waterways from silting up; the remainder represents new works. Future dredging operations are expected to show the same proportions.

Uncontaminated dredged material, if properly handled, causes few problems in the long term, and indeed can serve a variety of useful purposes, including land-fill, building of artificial reefs and reclamation of previously damaged coastal sites. If dumped at sea, its physical impact must be taken into account, and careful selection and management of the dump sites is important.

About 10% of dredged materials is contaminated from a variety of sources, including shipping, industrial and municipal discharges, and land run-off. Typical contaminants include oil, heavy metals, nutrients and organochlorine compounds. Dumped dredged material has liquid and suspended particulate phases, but the greatest potential for impact generally lies with the settleable or solid-phase material which may affect benthic organisms by smothering and physical disruption of habitats; bioaccumulation and toxicity from both soluble and suspended phases may also occur.

Contaminated dredged material may slowly release its adsorbed burden and result in long-term exposure of local habitats to one or more contaminants. However, laboratory and field studies show that leaching into the water column of chlorinated hydrocarbons, petroleum and metals is slight. Nutrients are released at concentrations much greater than background, but mixing processes tend to mitigate effects. The major impact at disposal sites with small current velocities and low wave-energy is the physical mounding of the material. Benthic recolonization of these mounds is relatively rapid on fine-grained sediments and slower on coarse-grained material.

No single method of sea disposal, or category of sea disposal site, is suitable for every type of dredged material or industrial waste. All alternatives need consideration at the planning stage to ensure that the waste has the smallest possible environmental impact. These include temporary containment or pre-treatment to reduce toxicity and oxygen demand, sea disposal beyond the edge of the continental shelf, and 'capping' of dredged material or wastes by placing them in depressions or pits sealed with clean sediment. There are alternative strategies by which sea disposal is concentrated at a single site or repeated as a cyclic operation over a more extensive area. Cycling will be more damaging if the capacity or time scale for recovery or recolonization of a slow-growing community is exceeded by too frequent discharges.

Mine tailings are of particular concern. It has been a common practice at coastal mines to dispose of waste materials to the sea either directly or by dumping into rivers from where the wastes are periodically swept to the sea during flooding. Some effluents are chemically inert, for example from china-clay mining, and the environmental effect is largely due to physical blanketing. For metal ore mining, on the other hand, operations extend from initial extraction-concentration activities to the final smelting-refining procedures. The resulting wastes are toxic, particularly those from the later stages, since the refined product often comes from intensive chemical treatment designed to isolate metals and their compounds. The main metal products from coastal mines and/or processing facilities are aluminium, copper, iron, lead, mercury, molybdenum, tin and zinc.

1.3.2   Industrial wastes and sewage sludge

Industrial wastes dumped at sea can present much more varied and intractable problems. They may be highly acidic or alkaline; liquid or largely particulate, and anything from relatively inert to extremely toxic. They include wastes from the chemical, petrochemical and pharmaceutical industries, from pulp and paper production, from smelters, from the food industry, from flue-gas washings and from military activities. Pre-treatment of wastes at industrial sites before disposal is judged to be essential in an increasing number of countries. LDC records show that in the period 1970–85 the largest amount of industrial waste dumped at sea was 17 million tonnes in 1982, and the smallest, 6 million tonnes in 1984.

The monitoring techniques used to assess the impact of waste disposal to the sea involve physical or chemical tests and species-diversity studies, but some are procedurally complex and costly, and all are difficult to interpret if not properly planned and carried out. Many of the data are not comparable between sites or studies because of the specificity of discharges, disposal sites and targets, and because standard procedures are not routinely used. Earlier studies are not always of direct practical use in environmental forecasting for new developments. Current monitoring strategies and practices in relation to the disposal of industrial wastes at sea should be reviewed to assess their effectiveness. Guidelines should be developed to ensure that all relevant variables and only the relevant ones are monitored.

The sludge arising from the treatment of sewage can be used as fertilizer on agricultural land or for land reclamation, when it is not contaminated with high levels of metals, oils and organic chemicals. However, in some cases it may be more economic and environmentally preferable to dispose of it at sea. Municipal sewage sludge normally does not contain contaminants in high concentrations, but excessive dumping may have harmful effects such as oxygen depletion and eutrophication, while health risks may arise from the presence of pathogens if dump sites are not carefully selected. Between 1980 and 1985, 15 million tonnes of sewage sludge were dumped at sea annually, although in recent years there have been strong moves in the USA and Western Europe to phase out marine dumping of sewage sludge. Accordingly, sewage disposal at sea is gradually decreasing, although this may continue to be more economic and environmentally preferable for those countries which currently do not have land-based sites for incineration or disposal.

1.3.3 Incineration at sea

For certain wastes, particularly organic materials in liquid form, the least damaging disposal option may be destruction by incineration. The technical requirements for complete destruction of the various wastes are known, including the temperature, residence time and level of oxygen supply in the furnace. When these requirements are met, the wastes are broken down to their basic components which are usually innocuous, and the output of the incineration process, apart from traces of any metals which may have been present, is largely NO_x, CO_2 and chlorine. Although this output can be minimized by scrubbing or neutralization, incineration sites on land are often resisted by neighbouring communities.

Incineration at sea is attractive in that remote sites can be designated and effects on the marine environment appear to be negligible. The optimal procedure for incineration at sea is to conduct it while the vessel is steaming clear of normal shipping routes in the open ocean. Liquid organohalogen compounds have been incinerated at sea since 1969, and in the period 1980–88 LDC reports show that the average amount was 100 000 tonnes per year, mainly in the North Sea. Incineration at sea is carried out in accordance with 'regulations for the control of incineration at sea of wastes and other matters' established under the LDC.

The arguments against incineration at sea are chiefly that there may be some reformation of toxic materials in the flue gases, that emissions may damage sensitive species in the sea-surface microlayer, and that the continued availability of this technology may act as a disincentive to reducing wastes at source. Fears have also been expressed that an accident may occur during transport to the burn site, although the likelihood of an accident is estimated (by the International Maritime Organization, IMO) at one occurrence per 68 000 voyages from European ports to the North Sea incineration site.

In 1988, all countries party to the Convention for the Prevention of Marine Pollution by Dumping from Ships and Aircraft, 1972 (Oslo Convention) agreed to phase out incineration at sea by 1994. The decision was not based on evidence of observed harmful effects but on the conviction that adequate means of disposal on land are or should soon be available to most of its contracting parties (mainly North Sea countries). Contracting parties to the LDC have also agreed in principle to discourage incineration at sea. In 1992 they will consider whether the practical availability of alternative, and more environmentally acceptable, technologies on a worldwide basis would be such that the practice should be discontinued.

On available evidence, the environmental implications of incineration at sea cannot be regarded as more significant than those of incineration on land. There are limitations and risks associated with either choice. In practice, the choice will depend on a careful analysis of technical, social and political as well as environmental factors. Pending the outcome of the 1992 LDC assessment, some countries, for instance small island countries, may find incineration at sea to be the preferred, or even the only, option for the disposal of certain wastes. For these reasons, GESAMP considers it appropriate to review the environmental aspects of this technology at an early date.

1.4   *Disposal of Plastic Litter*

The sea is inevitably the recipient of solid matter, intentionally disposed of or accidentally lost. This can interfere with fishing, shipping and other marine activities, but can also support life in the sea by providing additional surfaces for encrusting organisms and shelter for mobile species. In the past, much of such solid matter disintegrated quickly, but resistant synthetic substances have been replacing many natural, more degradable, materials and this trend is continuing.

There is now growing concern among fishermen, scientists, seafarers, conservationists and tourists about the increasing amounts of plastic material found at sea and on beaches. Such litter originates from both land-based and sea-borne sources. Most beaches near population centres are littered by a multitude of plastic residues washed up from the sea, contributed by rivers, ships and outfalls, dumped by illegal refuse operators or left behind by beach users.

Since most synthetic materials are buoyant and persistent, they present a threat to living organisms and the natural environment. Plastic debris can be loosely classified in three groups:

(1) fishing gear and equipment, such as nets and lines;
(2) packing bands, straps and synthetic ropes; and
(3) plastic litter, including bags, bottles, sheeting, packaging material and small pellets from which 'user' plastics are manufactured.

Such debris has been recorded, sometimes in large quantities, in the oceans, including the polar regions, and from intertidal areas to abyssal depths.

First, debris from fishing vessels causes a particular problem. Nets which are discarded or lost can continue to catch or entangle marine life and, being non-degradable, they may act in this way for years (ghost-fishing). They can trap marine organisms when floating on the surface, when snagged on the bottom, or when drifting at some intermediate level. Marine mammals, fish, sea birds and turtles are among the animals at risk. There is also a degree of human risk to workers underwater who may become entangled in abandoned netting. Debris can also seriously affect shipping by fouling propellers, damaging drive shafts and clogging sea intakes and evaporators. The loss in productive time at sea and the costs of repair represent a clear economic detriment to maritime industries, and, in the case of fishing vessels, can reduce earnings significantly. A 1975 estimate put the worldwide loss of fishing gear at 150 000 tonnes and this must now be significantly greater.

Second, plastic strapping and packing bands are another threat. They are used to hold palleted material, to secure cargo, to strap boxes and crates and to reinforce packing cases. When simply pulled off rather than cut, the bands float free in the sea and can encircle marine mammals or large fish in a girdle which becomes progressively tighter as the animal grows, inhibiting respiration and restricting the ability to eat or move. Plastic yokes for beverage packages and other containers represent a similar threat to birds and smaller fish. As with nets, there are many reports of animals caught in this fashion.

The third type of plastic debris consists of bags, containers, sheeting, packing material, raw plastic pellets and other similar items. In 1985 at least 450 000 plastic containers were dumped from the world's shipping fleet. Turtles, marine mammals and birds are killed by ingesting such material, while the increasing quantities and wider distribution of small plastic particles in the ocean are also causing concern, since they are ingested by marine organisms and, although inert, reduce the nutritional value of their food intake and consequently the animals' growth.

There is little argument that discarded plastics are harmful in the ocean environment, but agreement about the degree of harm and about effective steps to solve the problem is not easy to achieve because quantitative estimates of loss of marine life due to plastic pollution are difficult to obtain. Nor is it easy to compare, on present information, the amount of debris originating from land with that arising from fishing and shipping.

More study is needed to define the magnitude of the problem and to explore solutions. Better estimates of the number of marine animals killed and of the impact on the fishing and shipping industries are required. Research is needed on procedures for storing, and disposing of, synthetic materials, as well as on the design and manufacture of nets and other gear less harmful to the environment or more readily recoverable. Research is also required to develop alternative materials.

Some practical steps can be taken immediately. Packing bands and beverage yokes could be cut after use. All hazardous plastic products could be labelled to indicate their potential for damage to the environmental and marine life and the ways to minimize it. Fishing-net manufacturers might make parts of their nets, or the lines connecting them to floats or anchors, of degradable material to reduce the damage done by ghost fishing. Lastly, beach clean-up campaigns, which have recently been promoted in several countries, as well as removing litter, serve to raise public awareness, while providing evidence on the problem. The introduction of economic incentives and the development of guidelines and regulatory instruments should be explored as a means of encouraging the production and use of alternative materials that are not harmful to the environment, and to promote the collection and recycling of discarded plastics.

The International Convention for the Prevention of Pollution from Ships (1973), as modified by the Protocol of 1978 relating thereto (MARPOL 73/78), in its Annex V, contains regulations for the prevention of pollution by garbage from ships, which entered into force in December 1988. These include prohibition of discharge to the sea of all plastics, such as synthetic ropes, fishing nets and plastic bags. Guidelines for the implementation of Annex V to the Convention request governments to consider a series of measures, including reporting systems, record books on board ships, compliance incentive systems and educational programmes.

The abandonment of trash such as worn vehicle tyres, discarded domestic equipment, cans and crates contributes to the unseemly aspect of many shores, especially those close to urban areas. In some instances, even medical and surgical equipment has been reported on beaches.

Educational campaigns will be a powerful tool in bringing changes in public attitudes towards the environment, and such campaigns have indeed been introduced since 1988 by many contracting parties to the conventions or protocols for the prevention of marine pollution by dumping of wastes. Nevertheless, more effort should be directed towards convincing the public and the authorities of the value and small personal cost of keeping the environment clean – at sea and on the beaches as much as along rivers, inside cities and on mountain slopes.

1.5 *Manipulation of Hydrological Cycles*

Major changes in the pattern of river flows that are of significance to marine ecosystems can take place as a result of natural causes. The Yellow River in China, for example, has made several radical alterations of course during the past 4000 years, entering the Yellow Sea at points varying by as much as 800 km. The changes introduced by the deliberate actions of man in directly exploiting river hydrology must be viewed in this perspective.

Man-induced alterations of river flow date back to ancient civilizations, but major dam building did not begin until the early 20th century. The building of great multipurpose dams has accelerated since the 1950s with advances in engineering technology, particularly in the use of concrete. In the 1960s, 40 to 55 dams were completed each year, and recently the number of such schemes has increased substantially. In Africa and North America at least 20% of run off originates from impoundments; in Europe and Asia 15 and 14%; in Australasian and South American areas, 4 and 6%, respectively.

Rivers carry large amounts of dissolved and particulate material to the sea. Their discharges are highly variable, being determined by chemical, physical and biological factors in the river basin. The global amount of sediment reaching the oceans is $13.5 \ 10^3$ Mt y^{-1} but the paucity of accurate data, the difficulty of measurements during flood conditions and the degree of extrapolation needed make estimates uncertain. The major physical and chemical influence of river discharges in the coastal receiving waters depends on their flow, which will be altered substantially if the rivers are dammed. For example, the sediment discharge to the Mediterranean from the Nile dropped from about 150 Mt y^{-1} to almost zero after damming in 1965, the Zambezi sediment load appears to have dropped to less than half as a result of damming, and the contribution of sediment from the Colorado River to the Gulf of California has dropped from 135 Mt y^{-1} to less than 0.1 Mt y^{-1}. Reduced sediment load to coastal areas increases coastal instability and alters habitats.

Reduced and stabilized flow downstream from reservoirs can have direct effects on biological cycles in coastal waters and impedes the natural flushing out of accumulated material. Seasonal influences control the freshwater input to estuaries, which varies within 25% of the long-term annual mean, but upstream dams have significantly reduced both this variation and the freshwater discharge to estuaries. Impoundments have increased evaporative loss substantially, and changed the periodicity and timing of the flow.

In some coastal areas, extraction schemes have also reduced the groundwater contribution to river flow and have resulted in local subsidence and increased salinity of drainage water. One major effect is to increase the intrusion of the estuarine salt wedge inland, with significant effects on the flora and fauna of the coastal and nearshore zone. Mangrove swamps and rain forests in the Niger and Indus deltas have been severely damaged by salt-water intrusion. In many parts of the world there are significant effects on fish and other organisms that reproduce at the freshwater/ seawater interface.

Reduced water flow through manipulation of rivers has other effects on salinity regimes; a mean salinity increase of 0.19 per thousand is recorded in the Black Sea with increases of 2.0 to 2.5 per thousand in the Dnepr and Dnestr estuaries along with increased penetration of salt water. Loss of commercial fisheries has been attributed to a reduction of the brackish water environments where many species reproduce. Similarly, in San Francisco Bay, where freshwater diversion amounts to four times the volume of the Bay, fish populations have been greatly reduced. Changes in habitat associated with increased salinity may also produce favourable conditions for exotic species, and in the Sea of Azov this is thought to explain a massive invasion of jellyfish that has recently threatened indigenous species and caused public health and amenity problems.

Reduced freshwater flows will increase stratification in estuaries with far-reaching effects on their chemical and biological characteristics. In the Black Sea the destruction of mussel beds and the death of fish have been attributed to stratification with limited dilution and dispersion of organic materials, and consequent oxygen deficiency.

The construction of dams and the diversion of waters can have extensive consequences when a free-flowing river is the major source of nutrients for the coastal ecosystem. In the south-eastern Mediterranean the flood waters of the Nile previously supplied nutrients, stimulating a food chain that supported a major sardine fishery. With the completion of the Aswan High Dam in 1965, natural discharges virtually ceased. While some fresh water still reaches the Mediterranean, the suspended sediment load responsible for much of the earlier fertilizing effect is entirely held back. The effect on fisheries has been dramatic. Shrimp fisheries declined and the *Sardinella* yield of 18 000 tonnes in 1962 dropped to 2000 tonnes in 1967 and remained between 2000 and 3000 tonnes until 1983. There are now signs that the yield is rising again, possibly in response to increased nutrient inputs provided by drainage waters from the irrigation of agricultural areas in the delta and improved fishing methods. Major coastal developments have also far-reaching effects on the species composition of adjacent waters (e.g. the opening of the Suez Canal on Mediterranean species) or on the nature of the ecosystem (e.g. tidal dams and barrages). Other types of barriers placed across rivers, such as tidal control gates, can lead to local mortality in downstream coastal shellfish beds and suspended fish culture cages during high flows.

In conclusion, manipulation of hydrological cycles on land can have adverse effects in the marine environment by changing the structure of ecosystems, diminishing the yield of fisheries and altering coastlines. Clearly, while dams and diversions are planned to benefit agriculture or other human activities, a balance must be struck between the positive gains expected at a local level and the probable, but more remote, adverse effects on the overall environment.

1.6   Land-use Practices

While water diversion and dam building in inland areas have profound effects on the coastal zone by altering inputs of fresh water and sediments and by changing the physical characteristics of the coastline, a number of other activities conducted well inland also affect the sea and its resources. One of the most important of these is the intensive use of persistent agrochemicals, but deforestation, afforestation, irrigation and several other land-use practices are also significant. Their impact on the coast should be taken into consideration at the planning stage.

While it is apparent that large-scale clearing of forests and of grasslands generally results in more rapid run-off leading to soil erosion and increased sedimentation in coastal areas, the influence of trees varies with local topography, rainfall and soils. Large-scale afforestation in temperate climates has led to reduced river discharges by increasing evapotranspiration, and to changes in drainage-water quality, although the effect may vary according to edaphic and climatic conditions. Adverse effects also result from intensive farming practices. For example, intensive livestock rearing leads to high ammonia emissions with potential for soil acidification and more acidic drainage; overgrazing increases soil erosion, particularly in arid areas; disposal of animal wastes by land manuring or through sewers increases the organic load discharged to coastal areas.

The world-wide pressure to increase irrigation in arid areas has often led to adverse effects and will also have consequences in the long term for the marine environment. For example, irrigation water is often entirely consumed before reaching the coast, and any drainage from irrigated soils may be highly saline and contaminated by excess nutrients and pesticide residues.

Of the several topics discussed above, sediment merits special attention. It has been estimated that, as a consequence of human intervention, the natural global transport of sediment via rivers to the oceans has increased by a factor of almost three. As well as the sediment load arising inland from deforestation, agricultural practices, overgrazing and mining, there are contributions from coastal manipulations, marine mining and oil drilling. In all, these are long-term inputs and constitute a significant and progressive alteration to the global sediment flux from the terrestrial to the marine environment.

The impacts of sediment releases are varied and numerous. Before settlement, sediments in suspension affect primary producers in the plankton and, by reducing light penetration to the bottom, also cause alterations in sea-grass beds, corals and other benthic communities dependent on photosynthesis. High levels of suspended sediment also clog the gills of organisms filter-feeding from the water. After settlement, there is direct physical damage by smothering, but longer-term effects can follow from changes in the particle size of the substrate, with consequences for the structure of the benthic fauna. Further, since many contaminants adhere to particles, increased sediment input can bring increased loads of toxic chemicals.

In summary, the main impacts of enhanced sediment input to the marine environment are turbidity increase, smothering, altered substrate structure and toxicity. In the past, attention has been directed in this context to erosion, and the fate of sediments in the coastal zone has been seen largely as an engineering problem. It is suggested, however, that sediments *per se* may be regarded as pollutants under the GESAMP definition, and that in some parts of the world they constitute a major threat to coastal organisms. It is recommended that GESAMP should review the matter.

1.7 Transportation of Hazardous Substances

1.7.1 Oil

Marine transportation, including tanker operations, other shipping activities and accidental spills from ships, accounts for an estimated 46% of the total input of oil to the sea. Substantial changes in the amount and pattern of oil transportation by sea in the past decade are associated with economic and political changes, for example the pricing policy of OPEC and the hostilities in the Gulf area of the Middle East. After the events of the early 1970s, world oil consumption in 1979 was 3.1 billion tonnes but this declined following the price increases in the early 1980s, falling to 2.8 billion tonnes in 1985, largely as a result of reduced supply from the Gulf areas. Although the high prices discouraged consumption, they stimulated offshore drilling in deeper waters and more hostile environments. With the move towards stabilization of prices at lower levels in 1986, the trend in consumption has again been upward.

The general picture in the decade up to 1986 is of a dramatic drop of 25% in the amount of oil moved by sea, 431 million tonnes less in 1986 than in 1977. This reduction took place almost entirely in the Middle East, the 1986 exports from that area being only 53% of the 1977 figures, a reduction of 485 million tonnes. The main importing areas were still Western Europe first, the USA second and Japan third, but over the decade their imports were reduced by 34, 32, and 25%, respectively. Another notable trend has been the steady increase in the transport of finished products (mostly non-persistent) in contrast to crude oil. In 1977 the transport of finished products represented 15% of total exports but the figure had increased to 25% by the following year, and crude oil exports were 33% less.

Associated with the reduced transportation, the number of oil spillages at sea recorded by the International Tanker Owners Pollution Federation has declined steadily in the last decade, from an annual average of 670 events in the first five years to 173 in the last five. For major accidents with over 5000 barrels (725 tonnes) spilled, the corresponding averages are 20 and seven events. It is particularly encouraging that decreases occurred not only in the absolute numbers of accidents but also in the rate. An analysis of casualty reports in Lloyd's Register of Shipping shows that the number of serious casualties in tankers over 6000 gross registered tons (grt) average 2.5 per hundred ships in the period 1977–81 but only 1.8 in the period 1982–6. However, number is not the only aspect of casualties that must be considered, their magnitude and the circumstances in which they occur are as important (see Section 1.10).

The reduction in the amount of oil carried at sea has not only decreased pollution because of the diminishing numbers of accidents, it has also cut operational inputs of oil and this has been aided by the entry into force of MARPOL 73/78. Annex I of this convention requires, among other things, that a greater number of tankers be fitted with segregated ballast and crude oil washing systems, and that all must have effective oil/water interface detectors and overboard discharge monitors. Also, all vessels of 10 000 grt must be fitted with oil/water separators and oil discharge monitoring. In addition, special areas have been designated (Mediterranean Sea, Black Sea, Baltic Sea, Gulf Area, Red Sea and, since 1988, the Gulf of Aden) where there is total prohibition of all discharges from ships other than clean water.

These regulations have resulted in a major reduction of operational pollution, not only from tankers but also from all other types of vessel. There have been parallel national and international improvements in ship safety requirements and in traffic separation schemes in areas of high traffic density. In recent years there has been a major strengthening of enforcement procedures and vessel inspections, particularly by states that are major importers of oil.

1.7.2 Other hazardous substances

Hazardous substances other than oil may be transported at sea by dry-bulk carriers (e.g. sulphur, fertilizers), or by liquid-bulk tankers (e.g. petrochemicals, caustic soda solution, sulphuric acid) but most of the more hazardous chemicals (e.g. pesticides, weed killers, tetraethyl lead) are carried by container vessels and as packaged cargo on general dry-cargo ships, in accordance with the requirements of the IMO International Maritime Dangerous Goods Code (IMDG Code). In spite of this code, there has been damage to containers and loss of packages overboard and a continuing problem is the inadequacy of labelling and lack of description of the goods carried, which has caused difficulty in initiating prompt action for salvage and clean-up operations. While the transportation of oil at sea is well documented by reliable statistical information, similar information is not generally available for other hazardous substances, which vary in character, are produced by many different industries and number several thousand distinct formulations. These problems are even greater when the substances being transported are mixtures of hazardous wastes. Tighter control over shipping movements and in the administration and enforcement of regulations on transport of hazardous cargoes is required.

The movement of bulk chemicals in tankers has more than doubled in the past years, but the volume, approximately 25 million tonnes in 1985, is still small in comparison with oil. This includes several hundred different commodities, but more than 80% of the total tonnage is made up of 22 products. Of these, about half the bulk is contributed by 18 petrochemical products (of which nearly 60% is methanol, xylene, ethylene glycol, benzene and styrene) and the other half by caustic soda, phosphoric acid and sulphuric acid.

There are some well-documented accidents relating to containerized cargoes, drums of tetraethyl lead, pesticides and other substances. The problems arising from container ship accidents are exemplified by the wreck off Somalia in 1985 of the *Ariadne*, carrying 105 different chemical compounds, some highly toxic, which required a clean-up operation lasting nearly eight months. This episode also showed how informal co-ordination among international organizations can provide invaluable assistance to developing countries lacking the technical expertise to deal with such occurrences.

1.8   Exploitation of Non-living Marine Resources

1.8.1   Oil and gas

Sub-sea exploitation of oil and gas began in the 1920s. Although many individual fields were developed, each was small and located in shallow water near the coast. In more recent years, oil and gas have been found in many parts of the world in deeper waters further offshore and in a diversity of climates. Drilling operations are now conducted even in such hostile environments as the Grand Banks, parts of the Georges Bank and the Beaufort Sea.

Environmental impacts are possible at all stages of oil exploitation. During the initial surveys to locate reserves, the explosives used can kill fish, and other seismic survey techniques interfere with commercial fishing. When a field has been identified, assessment of its potential involves exploratory drilling from ships or temporary platforms, which produce the same impact as any large vessel anchored for an extended period. The discharges of drilling mud may cause additional problems. Once the presence of hydrocarbons in commercial quantities has been demonstrated, production facilities are set up. These may involve gravel islands created from dredged material from nearby borrow pits or from onshore gravel deposits, with material trucked to the island site over substantial causeways. Such islands cause multiple impacts both by the associated dredging and dumping and by physical alteration of coastal processes.

The most common method of exploitation is from steel or concrete production platforms which may weigh many thousands of tonnes. The impacts of these structures stem partly from operational releases and partly from accidents. To some extent the latter can be avoided by good safety practice. Operational discharges are for the most part regulated by international agreements. In the North Sea, for example, oil in water discharges is limited to 40 ppm. Both exploration and production installations use drilling muds, which may or may not contain significant amounts of oil, and produce large quantities of cuttings, rock fragments derived from the drilling. The cuttings, separated as much as possible from the drilling muds (which because of their high cost are recovered and re-used as frequently as possible) are disposed of over the side of the platform. They accumulate on the bottom and may affect an area of up to 3 km radius around the platform, and cause obvious changes in the benthic communities there. The impact of normal operations is therefore significant but localized. For instance, only about 0.1% of the North Sea is exposed in this way. Also, offshore wells can be a target for military action, as shown by recent events in the Gulf area, or sabotage, with consequent pollution of the neighbouring waters.

In addition to these environmental effects, oil exploitation has other impacts. The presence of rigs and pipelines creates exclusion zones for fishing vessels and other shipping, while the debris associated with offshore oil operations can damage fishing gear or entangle ships' propellers. In the North Sea, nearly six million pounds sterling have been paid out in compensation for loss of fishing gear by Norwegian fishermen and about 1200 claims have been made by UK fishermen over the past 10 years for loss of gear and fishing time. An operation over eight years to remove 1600 tonnes of debris from 6300 km^2 of sea bed in the Norwegian sector of the North Sea has cost an estimated three million pounds sterling. This clean-up in the Norwegian sector has been supported by improved charting of the sea bed, by serious attention by the oil companies to prevent debris being dumped and by stricter national regulations.

A further problem, only now emerging, is the question of decommissioning and disposal of oil installations. In some parts of

Table 1.1 The cost of removing existing oil platforms

	Number of platforms	Cost of total removal ($ million)
North Sea	83	7393
Gulf of Mexico	890	2037
Middle East/Gulf	445	382
West Africa	49	155

the world platforms are reaching the end of their useful lives and decisions must now be made on how to deal with them. If left in place they would need highly expensive maintenance but would be non-productive, unless some new use could be found for them. The cost of total removal of all existing platforms was estimated by the International Exploration and Production Forum of the Oil Industry as about 10 billion dollars in 1983, distributed among the various countries as shown in Table 1.1. These costs are seen as prohibitive by the oil industry, but, at least in the North Sea, any solution short of total removal will be opposed by fishing interests. Guidelines and standards for the removal of offshore structures have recently been developed by IMO, and guidelines for their disposal at sea will be developed within the framework of the LDC.

1.8.2   Other minerals

A small proportion of the commercially exploitable minerals in the sea is in a liquid phase as dissolved salts traditionally recovered by evaporation. The greater part is present as unconsolidated deposits – sand, gravel, shells, heavy metal placers, metalliferous muds, oozes and nodules. Others occur as consolidated deposits in crusts, mounds and stacks, or in tabular veins or mineralized channels or as beds in consolidated host rocks. Although a potential exists in deeper waters, most of the few economically recoverable deposits are on the continental shelves at depths of less than 200 m and may be expected to occur with the same frequency as on land, but would be more costly to develop. Each deposit might be exploitable for 15 to 20 years, depending on demand, rate of recovery and extent of new finds.

Two basic methods are used for mining solid deposits, scraping the surface and excavating a pit or trench. Scraping is employed where the deposits are at or near the surface, using dredge buckets or hydraulic action to lift the mined rock. Where the deposits are located within the sea bed, excavation techniques are preferred, ranging from the use of simple grabs and bucket-ladder dredges to anchored or trailing suction dredgers, or occasionally even drilling and blasting when the deposits are hard. In addition, borehole mining with recovery as a slurry has been used successfully for sand and sulphur offshore. Finally, tunnelling by conventional underground methods are occasionally been used for deposits of bedded coal, potash and ironstone and for veins of lead, copper and tin, the mines being entered from the shore or from natural or artificial islands in shallow water.

Effects will depend on the method of mining, the type of ore and the characteristics of the mine site, where disturbance will be caused in the water column and on the sea bed. In the water column, surface turbidity plumes are created by those systems designed to pump ore in a slurry to a surface vessel, and also occur close to the sea floor if fine material is produced or is already present in the bottom deposit. The main disturbances are on the sea floor in the path of the collection machinery, and additional disturbances by noise and even light are possible.

Effects may be in the near or the far field. Near-field effects are those limited to the mine site and the period of active mining. There will inevitably be local impact on the bottom. Immobile and slow-moving benthic species and their habitats are affected, and spawning grounds of other species are damaged by the mining machinery. On a sea bed subjected to wave action, shallow trenches in sand flatten in hours or months but in gravel, pits may take 25 years or more to fill. Such trenches, pits and mounds can cause problems for fishermen using bottom gear in the area, as can exposed or displaced boulders or discarded mining gear. Sand and gravel mining are effectively regulated in some countries.

Far-field effects are likely to be on the sea bed, surface and midwater effects being minimal. The two main factors are turbidity and sedimentation.

The direct physical effect of sedimentation is most important, although many burrowing organisms are able to work their way out as material is deposited. However,the scale and frequency of sediment discharge may exceed the capacity of benthic communities to survive or recover. Some organisms such as corals and bottom-spawning fish, which require clear water, are particularly at risk from increased sedimentation. Other communities, for example the cobble-kelp community in the Arctic, and deep-sea environments which are slow to be recolonized, are also particularly vulnerable. Toxic substances in the original sediments are unlikely to be a problem in the far field.

In conclusion, while mineral exploitation in the sea does have measurable impact on the environment, this is likely to be limited to the site and the time of the operation, and can be reduced by careful planning and attention to operational procedures. Widespread adoption of recognized standards and criteria for these procedures would be useful. Standardization of sampling, analyses and reporting of environmental information is desirable to obtain data that can be applied in different geographic or temporal contexts. Such data are required before the commencement of, during, and after the completion of mineral recovery operations so as to forecast and assess impacts.

1.8.3   Ocean energy development

Ocean energy technology includes ocean thermal energy conversion (OTEC), wave energy capture utilizing buoyed structures or coastal convertors, tidal energy capture by the damming of estuaries, potential capture of the translational energy of currents by mechanical or electromagnetic means and geothermal energy from the sea bed. The potential environmental effects of these activities are diverse.

OTEC involves the transfer of large quantities of cold, nutrient-rich bottom water to a warm surface environment and this may have still unassessed chemical and biological consequences in the vicinity of the discharge.

Operational installations based on wave energy are mostly small experimental schemes, used at present only for navigational lighting in remote areas. However, there is potential for the development of large installations. These would extend over several kilometres and would certainly have coastal impacts.

Tidal energy capture involves the damming of estuaries which have appropriate holding capacity and topography (length-to-width ratio), and high tidal range; there are few suitable sites worldwide. Some planned installations are very large and would result in substantial changes in the estuarine conditions and processes. There could be significant effects resulting from salinity change, reduced tidal flushing and loss or change of habitat by alteration of sediment regimes and flooding, particularly as the most suitable sites have narrow entrances backed by large embayments, often with extensive and productive marshlands important for wildlife and as fish nursery areas.

Capture of sea-current energy from free-standing or floating structures has been proposed, but no practical schemes have yet been developed. Likewise, the exploitation of the widely occurring submarine geothermal sources may offer possibilities in the future but is still at the research stage.

So far, ocean energy has been used on a very limited, and mostly experimental, scale. Concern about impending climatic changes due to continued emissions of CO_2 may, however, lead to restrictions on the use of fossil fuels and therefore favour alternative sources of energy that are currently uneconomic. Although at present the use of ocean energy is negligible, GESAMP should continue to watch developments in this field and their consequences to ocean health, and be prepared to review the subject in the light of changed circumstances.

1.9 Exploitation of Living Marine Resources

The first GESAMP report on the Health of the Oceans referred to the global fisheries yield, noting that the 1979 catch of 71.3 million tonnes represented an increase of about 1 million tonnes over the previous year and that annual increases were running at only 1–2%, much lower than the 6–7% increases of earlier decades. However, since 1979, the overall trend has been strongly upwards, with annual increases again in the region of 7%. The most recently reported catch, for 1987, achieved a new record of 92.7 million tonnes, and preliminary figures for 1988 indicate a further increase to 94 million tonnes. It is now expected that the figure of 100 million tonnes, which many believed to be the maximum sustainable global yield of conventional fisheries, will be reached well before the end of the century. However, this progressive increase conceals great variability of natural resources and many problems.

A major part of this variability is due to natural causes, not least to El Niño-type events (see Section 1.10) which result in changes in the distribution and abundance of the stocks of anchoveta and small pelagic fish, and alter the fishing patterns of several countries that contribute significantly to the global catch. In general, natural fluctuations are not clearly understood and their causes not known. Combined with excessive exploitation, the consequences for fisheries of these natural events seem to be much more important than any known pollution effect in open water.

A large number of stocks, especially those most valuable commercially, are fished at or beyond their maximum sustainable yield, and rational management is complicated by changes in the dynamic balances between species. Pressure on stocks is increased by new technology – the continued development of better vessels, improved fish-finding techniques, new gear, advanced handling and freezing facilities. Drift nets of monofilament nylon, for example, are now used on a large scale in the open ocean. In the South Pacific a fleet of 160 boats adopted this technique in 1988, and sets out each night over 60 km of netting, 60 m in depth, from each boat for tuna. A comparable operation takes place in the North Pacific for salmon. These nets catch dolphins, whales, turtles and seals as well as the target species and, used on a large scale, they represent a fishing effort that has not previously been thought possible in the open ocean.

Since the 13th century, whalers have been able to improve their catch by taking advantage of advancing technology to exploit more and more species, worldwide. Because whales are often dispersed through extensive sea areas and limited to slow rates of reproduction, the number of breeding animals within some of the most heavily exploited species is critical. While there is no firm evidence that any whale species has been lost, concern is expressed for species such as the Right Whale in the northern hemisphere, and the eastern Pacific Gray Whale. Formerly, the 'Blue Whale' unit system allowed Blue, Fin, Sei and Humpback whales to be hunted to quota limits. This procedure allowed continued exploitation even when the numbers of a species were dangerously depleted. More recently, because of this deficiency, individual species or stock catch limits were introduced in the mid-1970s, and this more rigorous control has been implemented by a management procedure specifying the limiting catch that would result in the maximum sustainable yield. This procedure gives protected status to populations which were judged to be at less than half of the original population size. Commercial whaling is currently in abeyance while a comprehensive assessment of the various stocks is being undertaken, and new management procedures are being formulated. This situation was under review in 1990. In the meantime whale hunting for scientific purposes continues.

As well as the effects on fisheries of natural events or of pollutants, the reverse situation should be considered, namely, the possible polluting role of fishery-related activities *per se*. Adverse effects can arise in a number of ways. Fishing operations can do physical damage to attached benthic plants and animals. Removal of large numbers of organisms alters population age structures and the composition and structure of food webs. Mariculture also has a variety of impacts, and all of these activities could influence the genetic structure of marine populations.

Fisheries exploitation has significant physical effects on the sea bed. Large modern demersal fishing vessels use extremely heavy gear with as many as 15 tickler chains weighing in total up to 12 tonnes in front of the trawl to stir up fish. The undersides of the nets are often protected by chain mats. Effects on the bottom range from insignificant ruts which may be smoothed over with each tide, to radical changes in the distribution of sediments and rocks which result in a general unevenness of the bottom, to the extent that the operations of fishermen using light gear in the same area are adversely affected.

Shellfisheries also contribute to sea-bed disruption. The gears used for harvesting clams, oysters, mussels and scallops leave ruts and trenches, and the effect of hydraulic dredging for molluscs is even greater. Apart from physical effects on the sea bed, the fauna can be affected directly. On hard ground, sessile invertebrate fauna such as corals and sponges are damaged and, even on soft bottoms of sand and mud, animals are destroyed and broken up, so that at intensively exploited sites the structure of the benthic animal community can be altered.

Biological effects of fishing arise from the reduction in numbers of fish and the consequent changed balance of grazing and predation pressures in the ecosystem. Sealing and whaling in the 19th and 20th centuries, particularly in the Antarctic, where some species were brought near to extinction, was followed by an increase in krill which was attributed to this reduced predation, but with subsequent increase in other consumers of krill, such as sea birds, and crabeater and fur seals. Similar, although less well documented, situations exist in other parts of the world. Thus it is now being suggested that penguin deaths at the Falkland (Malvinas) Islands were due to starvation attributed to overfishing of squid, and that mortalities of several species of birds, particularly puffins, in the North East Atlantic may be connected with the rise in industrial fisheries for small species and the juveniles of larger ones.

Human attempts to manage natural populations can have other effects. For example, conservation measures to protect seal stocks by preventing hunting and culling may increase their numbers, resulting in overcrowding and disease at haul-out sites and increased competitive pressure on fishery resources. In addition, seals are hosts to parasites, part of whose life cycle is completed in the flesh of commercial fish, and in several parts of the world fishermen complain that increased seal populations result in parasite levels in fish so high that the catch becomes unmarketable.

Although living marine resources are harvested largely for food, some species are utilized for other purposes. The exploitation of living corals, coralline algae and some molluscs for construction material can severely damage biological communities. The increasing importance and use of phamaceutical products from marine organisms has resulted in small-scale harvesting of rare or uncommon species.

Mariculture, which is rapidly expanding worldwide (25–30% per year in some countries), can also have substantial, if local, effects on the environment. If conducted on a large enough scale at a single site, it causes eutrophication, reduces visual amenity, and can interfere with other uses of the sea. In particular, cage culture brings together large numbers of fish in a relatively small space, releasing substantial quantities of uneaten food, and of faeces and other excreta. Less evident problems associated with mariculture are posed by the use of growth-enhancing and therapeutic agents and pigments. Of the vitamins, biotin and B12 have a short half-life in the sea but may stimulate plant growth briefly. Little is known about the fate of dosed pigments and antibiotics.

Another concern is the use of antifoulants to protect the nets, cages and other structures of fish farms. For example, organotin compounds have been found as contaminants of the environment around mariculture establishments in North America and the UK and have marked effects on non-target organisms. Other biocides recently introduced to protect salmon from ectoparasites, such as dichlorvos – an organophosphorus compound – are a cause of concern.

However, the most widespread pollution effects from cage culture are due to organic enrichment generated around sea cages where the organic content of sediments can be up to 20 times higher than in more distant, unaffected, areas. This results first in reduced species diversity, and in extreme cases the benthic invertebrates in the immediate vicinity of the cages are totally eliminated, with hypoxic conditions extending into the water column.

Comparable effects arise from mollusc (e.g. mussels) culture even when additional food is not supplied. On a global scale, the impact is small and the affected areas can be reduced by careful site selection and the use of improved culture systems, such as holding facilities which allow waste containment. However, where there is intensive cultivation and the available sites are limited, the local effect can be serious, and several governments have introduced licensing and other formal controls. Finally, in some parts of the world, particularly in southeast Asia and Central South America, the expanding culture of shrimp and fish has led to extensive elimination of mangrove forest areas, destroying nursery grounds for many coastal animals.

One feature of mariculture is the introduction of non-indigenous species, an event which may be planned but that has also long been known to occur as an inadvertent result of shipping movements or canal construction. In some cases, non-indigenous species of plants and animals thus introduced into an established habitat have been able to compete with, and displace, native species, and have brought in new pests and diseases. In Europe, for example, the Japanese seaweed *Sargassum muticum* was recorded in southern England and northern France in 1972 and, in spite of attempts to control it, is expanding its range, interfering with navigation and causing problems in harbours and on amenity beaches. For these reasons many countries have strict regulations controlling introductions, and the International Council for the Exploration of the Sea (ICES) has produced a Code of Practice concerning introductions and transfers of marine species.

Finally, there are possible genetic effects from the exploitation of living resources. Very high fish catches can so reduce the effective size of a stock that rates of genetic drift and of inbreeding might increase. The greatest genetic effect may be related to mariculture, since planned selective breeding could produce individuals better suited to market requirements but less fit to survive in the wild. It has been shown that escaped fish can often interbreed with wild individuals and there is a fear that, if this occurred on a large scale, it could degrade wild stocks, causing short-term disruption before natural competition eliminates the hybrids.

1.10 Extreme Events

1.10.1 Natural events

Natural catastrophes and other event-dominated changes are sporadic, with 90% of the impact perhaps taking place in 1% of the time. By definition they do not result from man's activities but their consequences are often magnified by human decisions, including the siting of settlements in high-risk areas. Among these natural events are storms (hurricanes, typhoons and cyclones) which, apart from the direct effects of the wind, can produce storm surges that do great damage to coastlines and coral reefs in many parts of the world, aggravating erosion and siltation and wrecking ships. Tidal waves (tsunamis), caused for example by underwater tectonic activity, resemble storm surges. In the Philippines the most severe tsunami in the present century occurred in 1976 and was generated by an earthquake south of Mindanao. It produced waves of 3 to 9 m height at the shoreline and the flood water reached 2 km inland, killing 8000 people. While the most dramatic effects were on human settlements (90 000 people were made homeless), beaches and mangrove stands were also severely affected.

Apart from disturbances due to such relatively frequent events, there are major anomalies of the atmosphere and ocean circulation that can cause widespread adverse effects. The best known example is El Niño. As a result of a sequence of complex meteorological and oceanographic events originating in the tropics and recurring at irregular intervals, warm (28–30°C) waters flow into the South East Pacific Ocean, especially off the coast of Ecuador, Peru and Chile. The 1982/83 El Niño was one of the most severe recorded and its consequences were dramatic. In 1983, the yearly rainfall in Colombia was twice the average. In June of the same year, rainfall was 40 times the monthly average at Guayaquil (Ecuador) and 340 times the monthly average at Paita (Peru). Rivers swelled and landslides destroyed entire slopes of the Andean ridges. Populated areas and agricultural land were swept by torrential water and mud flows, with major loss of human life. Sea level rose by as much as 40 cm and large swells striking the South American shore caused a retreat of the coast, inundated lowlands and destroyed fishing and aquaculture installations. The inflow of warm waters led to the immigration of tropical fish and the disappearance of commercial endemic species, halting the operation of fishing fleets, with a total loss to the fishing industry in Ecuador and Peru in excess of US$ 200 million.

Recurring natural disturbances are well documented also at the biological level, with many records of red tides, exceptional algal blooms and population explosions of a number of animal species, including jellyfish in the Black Sea and the Adriatic; the reef-burrowing sea urchin *Echinometra mathaei* in Kenya and Kuwait; the coral-eating gastropod *Drupella* in the Philippines, Japan and Okinawa, and the crown-of-thorns starfish *Acanthaster planci* in many areas. Population declines are also reported, such as mass mortalities of the sea urchin *Echinothrix* in Hawaii and throughout the Caribbean. On more local scales, there are many records of mortalities of marine organisms such as the sea birds in the Irish Sea in 1969, and of fish and invertebrates off the North East coast of North America in 1976 and off Norway in 1988, sometimes associated with unusual phytoplankton blooms. In addition, a viral epidemic has been killing thousands of common seals in the North Sea since early 1988. Paradoxically, some limited but recurring natural disturbance will, in many ecosystems, help maintain the ecological balance.

1.10.2 Accidents

In several of the foregoing sections, reference has been made to accidents, both ashore and at sea, as a source of marine pollution. The effects even of the most dramatic accidents occurring well inland, such as the Chernobyl accident (1986) and the Basel factory fire (1986), which polluted the river Rhine, were not, or barely, detectable in the sea. The accidents of greatest marine significance are more likely to be those which occur at installations directly on the coast, or on ships or rigs at sea. While a great diversity of chemicals may be involved, in the last decade most of the accidents have been associated with oil. The loading and unloading of cargoes and fuel tanks result in frequent, but usually small, spills at ports, terminals and storage facilities, but the major unplanned inputs of oil are from shipwrecks, blow-outs or other incidents at offshore platforms, or from undersea pipeline ruptures.

In the North Sea, 30 000 tonnes of oil were released over a period of eight days during a blow-out at the Ekofisk field in 1977. Much of this was ejected into the air at high temperature and pressure and evaporated, so that only a fraction of the oil was found in the sea and no toxic or ecological effects were evident. By contrast, the much larger Ixtoc blow-out off the Mexican coast (1979) continued for 10 months and 400 000 tonnes of oil were lost, producing an oil slick which spread across the Gulf of Mexico and contaminated beaches in Texas, damaging birds and marine life.

Tanker accidents are more frequent than major blow-outs and, since the *Torrey Canyon* wreck in 1967, many spills have been investigated intensively and are well documented. Tankers can spill up to 200 000 tonnes during a few days, but damage is related to the site of the spill as much as to its size. The 1989 *Exxon Valdez* spill of nearly 39 000 tonnes occurred in the narrow waters of Prince William Sound, Alaska, USA, and over 550 km of coast was contaminated, with birds and sea mammals killed, and shrimp, herring and salmon fisheries, as well as hatcheries, at risk in the immediate aftermath of the spill.

Long-term effects occur when oil is carried on to beaches, particularly in sheltered areas, and becomes buried in sediments, from which it may leach out and cause contamination for a decade or more. The polar regions, where oil degradation is slow, are recognized as being particularly sensitive to oil, but recent experience suggests that tropical habitats are also very vulnerable. A slick that reached the coast of Panama in 1986 killed between 51 and 96% of living subtidal coral within 3 m of the surface and up to 45% of coral between 9 and 12 m of the surface. Nearby reefs clear of the slick were not affected. A wide range of technical measures to combat oil spills is now available. These include the use of booms to protect sensitive areas, the collection of oil from the sea surface and treatment by relatively non-toxic chemical dispersants. However, anticipation, contingency planning and preparedness are essential to reduce the damage.

The economic and social costs of spills can be very large indeed, and include loss of living resources of commercial value, loss of tourist income, damage to ecosystems, reduced amenity value and high clean-up costs. The social costs of the *Amoco Cadiz* wreck were estimated in 1978 at between US$ 200 and 300 million. While some accidents are due to natural events such as storms, or to failure of equipment, most arise from human error. Their risk may be reduced by constant attention, adequate technology and good working practice, and the need for these cannot be overstressed.

Chapter 2

Marine Contaminants: Levels and Distribution

2.1 Transport and Fluxes

There is a wide diversity of pathways by which contaminants reach the marine environment. Over 40 000 km of actively divergent plate boundaries lie beneath the world oceans. Not only are the active areas a continuous major source of heat, but intermittent ejections of molten magmatic and hydrothermal fluids produce massive underwater clouds of sulphur and metallic compounds at high temperature. Such clouds or plumes with dimensions measured in tens of kilometres have been observed for example in the vicinity of the Explorer Ridge off British Columbia and thermal vents have been detected in many ocean areas. Few quantitative data are yet available on these natural inputs, but their magnitude implies that they are significant on a global basis. However, the two dominant pathways by which potential pollutants reach the oceans from the continents are rivers and the atmosphere. If these inputs to the oceans are to be controlled, attention should be directed to the processes by which contaminants initially become entrained in rivers and atmosphere. To judge the need for, and value of, such controls, some assessment of the relative importance of each pathway is required.

2.1.1 River input to the sea

The land–sea flux from rivers can be considered as made up of the gross flux, i.e. the rate of contaminant transport to the sea from within the river catchment itself, and the net flux, i.e. the flux of river-derived material that escapes from the nearshore and estuarine region and is transported to the open ocean.

The most reasonable way of estimating the global gross flux from rivers to oceans is to extrapolate flux data obtained from rivers representing a range of climatic, geological, biological and demographic regimes for which reliable data are available. At present, this is possible for only a small number of river systems and a few contaminants. In dealing with nutrients, for example, a variety of river systems has been studied and the results extrapolated to provide an estimate of the total global gross river input, giving figures for the natural fluxes of dissolved nitrogen, phosphorus and silicon and for the fluxes of suspended nitrogen and phosphorus.

The fluxes resulting from human activities have also been estimated by a variety of other approaches, including comparison of pristine and polluted rivers, historical evolution of concentrations in some large rivers, and direct estimation of fluxes due to discharges from domestic, agricultural and industrial activities. Although there are large discrepancies between the various estimates, it can be said that the anthropogenic flux of dissolved nutrients is at least comparable to, and in some areas significantly greater than, the natural flux.

For trace metals there are considerable uncertainties but available flux estimates are likely to be in error by not more than an order of magnitude. The complex chemistry of synthetic organic compounds and their large variety suggest that estimates should be made on a compound-specific and regional, rather than on a global, basis.

The net flux to the open ocean must be determined at some offshore boundary because many of the chemicals transported by rivers to the sea are transformed or removed from waters as they flow seawards over the shelf. Calculation of the net flux also permits estimates of the fraction of riverborne material that is retained on the shelf. The longer the residence time of water on the shelf, the higher this fraction will be, so that rivers discharging to enclosed marginal seas will make smaller net inputs to the deep ocean than rivers opening directly on to narrow well-flushed shelves.

2.1.2   Atmospheric input to the sea

The atmosphere carries material from many sources, natural and anthropogenic. The former include dusts from arid areas, soil, volcanoes, vegetation and forest fires, as well as aerosols from the oceans. Among the anthropogenic sources are emissions from industries, energy production and use, waste combustion and agricultural activities. Sources of synthetic organohalogen compounds to the atmosphere include emissions during production and disposal, as well as during applications of pesticides, for example. Contaminants can disperse in the atmosphere as gases or as aerosols and fine particulates – an important distinction because it affects the rate, mode and site of deposition. These compounds are injected into the atmosphere near ground level. From there they are mixed vertically and can then be transported thousands of kilometres across national boundaries and spread to major oceanic systems.

Since sources of contaminants are mainly in mid-latitudes in the northern hemisphere, materials tend on balance to move from west to east, although in the case of specific events (e.g. the Chernobyl accident) weather conditions at the time of release determine the paths of the emissions. In general, North America contributes to the North Atlantic Ocean, and the Asian continent influences the North Pacific and Arctic Oceans. On the other hand, movement in the trade wind zone is from east to west, so that the flow from southern North America is across the north Pacific and from north Africa to and across the north Atlantic. A variety of meteorological models describe these atmospheric movements and incorporate emissions, transport, chemical transformations and removal processes.

The total atmospheric input of chemicals to the ocean surface is the sum of the amounts entering directly in gas and particulate phases (dry deposition) and of those falling out as rain and snow (wet deposition). It is difficult to obtain an accurate estimate of either. Even when contaminant-free samples of precipitation are available, and this is particularly difficult to achieve over the oceans, interpretation of the data is complicated because chemical composition varies with differences in vertical distribution, duration, intensity and droplet size of the precipitation. Even greater difficulties are encountered in making direct measurements of 'dry' particulate deposition. Finally, techniques are not at present available to make direct measurements of the relevant gas fluxes across the air/sea interface.

Because of these problems, indirect methods have been developed for the estimation of contaminant fluxes. Most estimates are of gross rather than net flux, since some chemicals entering the ocean from the atmosphere can be re-injected to the atmosphere via bursting bubbles or gas exchange. Unless this recycled material can be taken into account, the calculated deposition may be anomalously high. Existing data bases suitable for estimating the air/sea flux vary in size and quality, and few are extensive enough

in time and space to take account of the variability in atmospheric
(and water) concentrations and deposition rates, although this is
improving in some ocean basins, particularly the North Atlantic
and North Pacific.

Some data are available from the North Sea, the Baltic Sea and
the western Mediterranean, as well as from areas of the Pacific
and Atlantic Oceans. Extensive evaluation of data from these and
other sites indicates that atmospheric fluxes of many metals (excluding mercury) to the North, Baltic and Mediterranean Seas are
3 to 10 times higher than those to the open North Atlantic. Fluxes
to these regional seas are 10 to 100 times higher than those to the
tropical North Pacific, while fluxes to the South Pacific are lower
than those to the North Pacific by a factor of between five and
ten. These flux differences are consistent with the increasing
distances from continental sources, both natural and anthropogenic. Mercury shows relatively small flux differences because
it is found in the atmosphere primarily in the gas phase as ele-
mental mercury, which has a relatively long atmospheric lifetime
and therefore a relatively homogeneous geographic distribution.

Similar atmospheric flux estimates have been made for some
high molecular weight organic compounds such as polychlorin-
ated biphenyls (PCBs), DDT and hexachlorohexane (HCH) to the
European regional seas as well as the open Atlantic and Pacific
Oceans. Although there are even greater uncertainties, a trend of
decreasing atmospheric fluxes can be seen between the regional
seas and the northern hemisphere open oceans of roughly a factor of between two and five, with fluxes to the southern hemisphere oceans generally a factor of two to five lower still. The overall decreases in flux are less than for most of the metals studied
because, like mercury, the organic compounds are found predominantly in the gas phase and have a longer atmospheric residence time than metals associated with aerosol particles.

Finally, the fluxes of fixed nitrogen species show the same type
of gradient from the regional seas to the South Pacific, but the
gradient is again less marked than for metals, despite the short
atmospheric lifetime of fixed nitrogen. This may reflect important
sources of fixed nitrogen in remote marine areas.

2.1.3   Comparison of river and atmospheric inputs

On the basis of this information, comparisons of river and atmospheric fluxes to the marine environment can be made for several
substances. Calculations indicate that approximately 98% of the

lead which eventually dissolves in sea water enters the global ocean via the atmosphere and that most of the dissolved cadmium, copper, iron, and zinc are also primarily derived from the atmosphere. The inputs of arsenic and nickel from the atmosphere to the global ocean are also significant. Atmospheric inputs account for between 80 and 99% of PCBs, DDT, hexachlorobenzene (HCB) and HCH found in open ocean sea water. Atmospheric sources of polyaromatic hydrocarbons (PAHs) and HCH clearly exceed river inputs to the North Sea.

Turning to nutrients, comparison of the contributions of atmosphere and rivers to the world ocean shows that the atmospheric input of nitrogen species is considerably greater than the net input from rivers, the atmospheric contribution being comparable to the gross river input. The atmospheric input of phosphorus is roughly the same as that entering from rivers. Estimates of river fluxes, direct discharges and atmospheric fluxes to the North Sea lead to the conclusion that the river inputs of nitrogen there are similar to those for the Mediterranean.

In conclusion, the information available suggests that river inputs are generally more important than those from the atmosphere in coastal zones, although in certain areas and for some substances (e.g. lead and HCH in the North Sea, nitrogen in the Mediterranean) atmospheric inputs are similar or even dominant. In open-ocean basins the atmospheric flux of man-made contaminants is generally more important than the net input from rivers for many substances because the river flux material is largely captured within the coastal zone. However, the paucity and relative inaccuracy of data must be emphasized. In particular, there is an almost complete lack of river and atmospheric input data collected simultaneously in the same marine area, and steps should be taken to improve the data base.

2.2 Contaminants of General Concern

2.2.1 Synthetic organic compounds

In addition to the well-known contaminants, between 500 and 1000 new chemicals are introduced to the market every year, and known chemicals are turned to new purposes. Their environmental fate and consequences are seldom known. Thus, concentrations of bound chlorine in fish fat range from 30 to 200 ppm in most samples, of which 5 to 10 ppm are attributable to known contaminants such as DDT, PCBs, dioxins and chlorophenols. The rest (up to 95%) is unaccounted for. Possible sources may be low-molecular-weight compounds from pulp mills, from aluminium and magnesium smelters and from the burning of chlorine-containing materials. Clearly, much more needs to be known about the life history of chlorinated compounds released to the environment.

Chlorinated hydrocarbon pesticides and PCBs are a source of special concern because of their persistence in the environment, their concentration along food chains and their long-lasting storage and accumulation in the fatty tissues of animals, reaching the highest levels in raptors and marine mammals. These substances, after reaching the sea mostly through the atmosphere, become adsorbed to suspended particles and tend to settle in sediments. They will remain there until mobilized by disturbances of the sea floor and so possibly reintroduced into the food chain, regardless of whether their use has been discontinued on land.

Data on production and use of pesticides and PCBs are lacking for most parts of the world. In most countries in the temperate latitudes chlorinated pesticides have been banned and are being replaced by less persistent products. PCBs have been used since the 1930s for a number of purposes – as dielectrics in transformers and capacitors, from which they can normally be recovered without loss, and as hydraulic and heat-transfer fluids as well as components of a number of products such as paints and lubricating oils. When not used in strictly controlled closed systems, they can spread and eventually reach the sea. Despite the phasing out of their use in non-closed systems in a number of countries, they continue to be released to the environment, for instance from dumps and landfills. In lower latitudes, environmental measurements indicate that chlorinated pesticides, including DDT and HCH are widely applied, and suggest that the use of PCBs is increasing. As a result, DDT, HCH and PCBs are now clearly measurable even in the Antarctic environment, although at levels lower than in temperate latitudes.

While global time trends in the concentrations of these substances are not known because improved analytical techniques make it difficult to compare past and present results, there is strong evidence that ocean surface waters have highest concentrations in the northern temperate latitudes and lowest near the poles. Likewise, specimens of marine mammals from the northern hemisphere have higher levels of PCBs in their fat than those from the southern hemisphere. The latitudinal difference is less for DDT.

The biocidal properties of organotin compounds, especially tributyltin (TBT) were recognized in the early 1950s. Initially, these substances were used as fungicides, bactericides and preservatives for woods, textiles and paper, and for electrical insulation. TBT was first introduced as an antifouling agent in marine paints in the mid-1960s. It also enters the marine environment as a result of a variety of other uses. For instance, it is, or has been, applied in antifouling preparations on the net cages used in salmon farms, and it is used in some countries on lobster pots and ponds for keeping fish and shellfish. It was known to be highly effective, and laboratory tests suggested that, since it degrades quickly, any side effects should be minimal. While it did prove to be a most effective agent in the protection of ships and other structures from fouling organisms, its continued use made it more persistent than expected, and effects on some marine organisms were detected at very low concentrations.

Its impact on non-target species was first noted in the mid-1970s in Arcachon Bay, which supplies about 10% of the oysters consumed in France, but is also a major recreational area with a large number of pleasure craft, often berthed in marinas close to areas of oyster production. Oysters (*Crassostrea gigas*) there had begun to show serious shell malformations and the natural spatfall of this species and of the European flat oyster (*Ostrea edulis*) was seriously reduced. Leaching of TBT from the anti-fouling paints used on the boats was suspected, and experiments involving leachates from painted panels confirmed the link.

After the first reports by French workers, similar problems were found in several other countries. Detailed further work, particularly in the UK, confirmed that TBT was the cause of shell malformations in *C. gigas* and that it also caused reproductive failure in *O. edulis*. Shell malformations in *C. gigas* were detected at concentrations down to at least 200 ng l^{-1}, and similar concentrations clearly inhibited reproduction in *O. edulis*. Growth of newly metamorphosed larvae of the species was reduced at 60 ng l^{-1} and slightly affected at 20 ng l^{-1}.

The side effects of TBT are not confined to oysters. A wide range of non-target organisms (fish, tunicates and most of the main marine invertebrate groups) all show some effects at concentrations of tenths of ng l^{-1}. The common dogwhelk (*Nucella lapillus*) has proved to be particularly sensitive, incurring 'imposex' (females develop male characteristics) at exposures as low as 2.5 ng l^{-1}. Monitoring in a number of countries, especially the USA and Canada, has confirmed the existence of such concentrations at a wide variety of sites. Although TBT in clear sea water breaks down in 7 to 15 days, it persists longer in estuaries because of decreased light penetration and sorption on to particulate matter in the water column and on to sediments.

No public health hazards due to accumulation of TBT in marine organisms for human consumption have been demonstrated, but detailed assessments are in progress. However, the unwelcome impacts on non-target organisms have led some countries to restrict or prohibit the use in antifouling paints. The first of these actions was taken by France in 1982 with a ban on TBT-based paints on pleasure craft less than 25 m in length, other than those constructed of aluminium. The UK followed with restrictions on certain paints in 1985, and in 1987 all uses of TBT preparations were prohibited, except those involving low concentrations in copolymer-based paints intended for use in commercial shipping. Several other countries have introduced or are considering introducing regulations. In the USA many states have adopted restrictions. The restrictions are based on good evidence and should be extended.

Results of continued environmental monitoring after the restrictions had been imposed in France suggest that recovery of the affected environments can be expected within two to five years. But recent observations indicate that hazardous concentrations are still found in some areas. The experience with DDT suggests that a watch should be continued on TBT uses and fate, as well as on the possible effects of its substitutes.

2.2.2 Radionuclides

Radioactive substances are present naturally in ocean waters. Among these are radioisotopes of potassium, rubidium, thorium and uranium, the last two always accompanied by their radioactive disintegration products. Other radioactive substances, such as ^3H and ^{14}C, originate in the atmosphere through the interaction of cosmic radiation from outer space and the constituents of the air, and can also be produced in the course of human activities.

The first group reaches the oceans mostly as a result of run-off from weathered rocks or, in the case of their disintegration products, by decay of the primordial substances in the water itself. In contrast, cosmogenic radioactive substances are deposited on the surface of the ocean by precipitation. Both categories of substances are then distributed through the water column by physical, chemical and biological processes, and subsequently deposited in the ocean sediments. The inventories of, for example ^{14}C,

^{3}H, ^{40}K and ^{238}U in ocean waters have been estimated to be 8.0×10^3, 8.5×10^2, 1.6×10^7 and 5.6×10^4 PBq (petabecquerels), respectively.

Human activities add to the inventory of ocean radionuclides. Naturally-occurring radionuclides are leached from mine tailings and milling wastes but give rise to measurably increased levels only close to their sources. Elsewhere, their contribution is negligible or at least not measurable.

Nuclear weapons tests have introduced artificial radionuclides into the environment. Most of these have arisen from tests in the atmosphere and fallen out through dry and especially wet deposition. Artificial radionuclides produced by such tests include ^{14}C, ^{137}Cs, ^{3}H and ^{90}Sr, as well as plutonium and other transuranic elements. Rough estimates of the inputs of these radionuclides to the oceans have been derived from information reviewed by the United Nations Committee on the Effects of Atomic Radiation (UNSCEAR) in its 1982 report. The estimates of input were 6.1×10^2, 1.5×10^5, 8.2 and 3.7×10^2 PBq for ^{137}Cs, ^{3}H, $^{239, 240}$Pu and ^{90}Sr, and not less than 40 PBq for ^{14}C, respectively.

The inputs to the oceans in the southern hemisphere have been half of those in the northern hemisphere. Recently an Intenational Atomic Energy Agency (IAEA) Expert Group has obtained slightly higher estimates of the ocean inventories of these radionuclides on the basis of measured concentrations. Fall-out from nuclear tests has been the only source of worldwide radioactive contamination of the oceans. However, its widespread dispersal has resulted in low-level ambient concentrations and hence in negligible additions to the exposure from natural background.

Operational discharges of effluents containing radioactive material from nuclear reactors and reprocessing plants make an additional contribution to the radionuclide inventory. The discharges are allowed under regulatory controls, which include authorization and monitoring, and reach the oceans through the atmosphere, rivers and, in some cases, from direct releases to the marine environment. The total amount of artificial radionuclides entering the ocean from the nuclear fuel cycle, and as a result of industrial and medical uses, is difficult to assess. However, recent estimates of the maximum annual inputs from the nuclear power plants currently in operation have been derived for a number of radionuclides by an Expert Panel (established within the framework of the LDC), on the basis of information regularly reviewed by UNSCEAR. Regarding the releases from fuel reprocessing plants, it should be noted that only 5% of the fuel is reprocessed at present, and that discharges from plants currently in operation are decreasing. Thus, according to the latest UNSCEAR report, discharges from Sellafield, UK, were 2.7 PBq in 1980–81, 1.6 in 1982–83 and 0.38 PBq in 1984–85; from Cap de la Hague, France, the ^{137}Cs releases were 0.039 PBq in 1980–82 and 0.027 PBq in 1983–85.

Some low-level radioactive wastes have in the past been packaged and dumped at sea. This practice, however, was discontinued, at least temporarily, in 1982 as a result of a voluntary moratorium, consistent with a non-binding resolution of the contracting parties to the LDC. From 1946 to 1970, 4.5 PBq of radioactive waste were dumped in about 90 000 containers in the Atlantic and Pacific Oceans and in the Gulf of Mexico. Those dumped by western European countries between 1949 and 1982 consisted of 54 PBq in some 140 000 tonnes of packaged wastes at 10 sites, predominantly in the vicinity of latitude 46°N and longitude 17°W. Comparatively small dumping operations were also carried out by Japan between 1965 and 1968 and by the Republic of Korea between 1968 and 1972.

The total amount of radioactive material dumped at sea, some 60 PBq, is much less than the approximately 2×10^5 PBq that were added to the oceans as a result of atmospheric nuclear weapons testing between 1954 and 1962. This, in turn, is only 1% of the 2×10^7 PBq that exist naturally in the ocean. However, the mix of radionuclides involved is different in each case. Because radionuclides vary widely in the extent to which they can affect marine organisms and man, their total activity is only a very rough guide to risks. It must also be stated that dumping cannot be considered safe just because releases of radionuclides are small compared with the natural incidence of radionuclides in the environment. The Expert Panel set up under the LDC concluded that:

(a) The present and future risk to individuals from past oceanic dumping of radioactive waste is extremely small. The risk (of developing a fatal cancer or severe hereditary defect) is predicted to peak about 200 years from now at a level of less than 10^{-9} per annum. The individuals with highest potential exposure would be those consuming shellfish harvested in Antarctic waters.

(b) Notwithstanding the very small risk to individuals, the aggregate exposure of the global population from long-lived components of the dumped waste imply that the total casualties resulting from past dumping may be up to about 1000 cases spread over the next 10 000 years or so. The dominant pathway for this exposure would not be via shellfish consumption, but associated with the consumption of food produced on land. The reason for this is that the main contributor to these casualties (or to the collective dose commitment, as it is known technically) is the isotope ^{14}C which has a half-life (i.e. time required for its activity to decrease by 50%) of 5700 years. Over such a period much of it would escape from the ocean as gaseous carbon dioxide and spread throughout the world. If ^{14}C, and a few other long-lived radionuclides, were to be removed from the waste before disposal in the ocean, the collective dose commitment from future dumping operations would be very much reduced, although it should be appreciated that other means of disposal of ^{14}C might carry risks comparable to those associated with sea dumping.

(c) The incremental dose from past dumping to individual marine organisms on the sea floor at the dump site or nearby will be significantly less than the dose that the organisms receive from naturally occurring radionuclides, and hence is not expected to cause any detectable effects on populations of organisms.

Radionuclides in the sea may contribute to internal or external exposure of organisms, including man, through several pathways. Those related to internal exposure are the consumption of various types of seafood and the inhalation of airborne particulates and marine aerosols. External exposure may occur during swimming, boating and other beach activities. It may also result from the handling of contaminated fishing gear. Some pathways, while of scientific interest, do not lead to significant exposure from radionuclides. For instance, bubble scavenging in the water column coupled with droplet ejection from bubbles bursting at the surface may be a mechanism for transfer of radionuclides and heavy metals from sea to air and subsequently to land. This has been demonstrated for plutonium and americium in the Irish Sea, but the radiation dose from large droplets introduced in the surf zone is negligible compared with that received by the critical group from seafood consumption. However, small droplets generated by bubble bursting may make a measurable contribution to levels of plutonium near the coast.

Nuclear accidents have not contributed significantly to the ocean inventory of radionuclides on a global scale. Although three major nuclear accidents (Windscale, UK, 1957; Three-Mile

Island, USA, 1979 and Chernobyl, USSR, 1986) have resulted in radionuclide releases to the environment, the major pathways leading to man were not marine. In the Windscale accident, the principal route for irradiation of man was radioiodine in milk. At Chelyabinsk exposure resulted mostly from ^{90}Sr-contaminated milk and from external irradiation. At Three Mile Island most of the release consisted of radioactive noble gases, especially ^{133}Xe. The releases from the Chernobyl accident gave rise to widespread contamination of the environment throughout Europe and to exposures of the population mainly from gamma emitters deposited on the ground and from ^{137}Cs in dairy and meat products. The deposition of ^{137}Cs in the oceans was estimated to be 4.7 PBq out of the total of 70 PBq released. The exposure of people through consumption of seafood was negligible, and no effects on marine organisms were observed.

Ocean waters also received ^{238}Pu from the isotopic generator of a satellite that disintegrated in 1964 on accidentally re-entering the atmosphere. In the coastal waters off Greenland plutonium levels slightly increased following the accidental loss of two nuclear weapons in 1968.

The manufacture and operation of military nuclear equipment, as well as the operation of nuclear powered ships, must also make a contribution to the inventory of radionuclides in the oceans, but no information is available on these sources of contamination.

The concern about radioactive substances in the oceans stems from the potential harmful effects of the emitted radiation on organisms, particularly man. This depends on the doses received by the targets, i.e. on the energy absorbed by living tissues from sources outside them (external irradiation) or emitted by radionuclides deposited in the tissues (internal irradiation) after ingestion or inhalation.

In the case of man, harmful effects of radiation are well recognized but at doses orders of magnitude higher than those from natural sources. For levels of radiation comparable to environment levels, quantitative risk factors have been developed for planning purposes. Thus, the lifetime dose limit (1 mSv y^{-1}) used to protect members of the public from all planned sources of radiation excluding medical sources is equal to one half of a year's average exposure to natural radiation. Maximum annual doses to critical groups via marine pathways from dumping at sea are, for example, more than a thousand times lower than the dose limit. Radiation doses arising from reprocessing plant releases are higher than from power plants, a representative value being one tenth of the annual average dose from natural background. However, in some cases (i.e. Sellafield, UK), they are higher, the most exposed group receiving a dose close to twice natural background in the year of maximum exposure.

Doses to, and effects on, marine organisms or marine populations are much less well known. As in man, effects may be somatic (in the individuals exposed) or genetic (in the germ cells of the irradiated individuals and therefore transmissible to their descendants). While for man the individual is the target of concern, for marine organisms interest is primarily in population effects such as survival, growth and reproductive performance. However, at the levels at which the populations of marine organisms are currently exposed as a result of man-made inputs of radioactive materials, adverse effects have not been observed.

2.2.3 Petroleum residues

Oil affects wild life and environmental quality directly and is highly visible and easily recognizable. This may account at least partly for the concern still widely expressed about it as a marine contaminant. The major source of input to the oceans is from shipping, which is dealt with in Section 1.7. Spills in restricted areas have dramatic local impact, as discussed in Section 1.10. This section discusses an aspect which is causing problems around the world, pollution from the most persistent fraction, oil tar. This originates when evaporation of the light fractions of hydrocarbon compounds released to the sea leaves flakes, lumps or balls which float and are distributed widely by winds and currents. About 1% of oil released to the sea forms floating tar, and much of this originates from tanker sludges, but a variety of other sources contribute. Tar eventually drifts on to beaches and accumulates there.

In some parts of the world where shipping, particularly tanker traffic, is heavy, especially in semi-enclosed seas, the effect on beaches can be dramatic. In the Red Sea, for example, and in the Kuwait/Oman area, which probably receive more oil pollution than anywhere else in the world, tar abundance on beaches is sometimes as much as 100 times higher than in other regions. Weights of 1 kg m^{-1} of coastline are common in this region, and values of up to 30 kg m^{-1} occur. In places, weathered oil pavements many centimetres thick blanket sandy beaches and rocky promontories and cover the aerial roots of mangroves. These are extreme conditions, but the situation in many other parts of the world also gives cause for concern. For example, in the wider Caribbean, which is a region of very significant hydrocarbon production, oil is an ubiquitous marine contaminant, damaging the important tourist industry. It is estimated that the use of beaches by tourists is adversely affected when tar levels reach 10 g m^{-1} of beach front. Many beaches in the Caribbean have average concentrations in excess of 100 g m^{-1}, a level at which beaches become virtually unusable for recreation. A comparable situation is found for Indonesia and the Philippines, in India (particularly its West coast) and Pakistan, in parts of West Africa and the Mediterranean, and, although with less impact, at most windward beaches in other parts of the northern hemisphere. By contrast, many beaches in the southern hemisphere are relatively unspoiled.

There is broad agreement, confirmed by many surveys, that since 1979 there has been a significant reduction in beached tar around the world. In some countries this can in part be accounted for by systematic and regular cleaning of beaches. Two more general factors are the reduction in marine transportation of oil following the price crisis of 1979 and the entry into force in 1978 of the 1969 amendment to the international convention OILPOL 54. This amendment permits the release of oil from tankers only in restricted areas and, even there, only at certain rates and quantities. Further, MARPOL 73/78, which replaces the OILPOL Convention, in its Annex I (which entered into force in 1983) provides for the designation of 'special areas' within which tight control of pollution is required, and this has been adopted, for example, in the Mediterranean Sea. There is, however, no cause for complacency. Many beaches remain spoiled by tar, and a more stringent enforcement of the relevant regulations is desirable.

2.3   *Concentrations in Water, Sediments and Organisms*

Since the first GESAMP Review, a large amount of additional and more reliable information has become available on the concentration and distribution of contaminants from many parts of the world, as a result both of large-scale international surveys and of more restricted national exercises. Also, as indicated below, there have been improvements in sampling and analytical techniques and in data quality management generally. This section begins with a consideration of data quality, then focusses on the most critical potential pollutants within each class for which systematic measurements are available on a wide geographical basis – selected trace elements, nutrients, DDT and PCBs. In selecting and presenting data, coastal and open-ocean zones have been differentiated where this appears to be useful and, from the innumerable analyses of organisms, examples have been selected from species of economic importance or bioindicator value.

Concentrations in water are given as mass/volume ratios (e.g. μg l^{-1}); in sediments and tissues as relative dry weights (e.g. ppm), except where otherwise indicated.

2.3.1 Quality control and data validation

If environmental assessments are to be valid, the chemical measurements on which they are based must be reliable and adequate for their intended use. This is specially important where the information is to be used for decision making and the enforcement of regulations or for legal purposes.

It has recently become clear that many chemical measurements in the sea made more than 10 years ago are dubious, making it difficult to establish time trends where changes in concentration develop over a longer time scale. The inaccuracy of past data has become apparent as new analytical techniques and quality-control procedures have been developed, and recent measurements of ambient concentrations are lower than those previously reported. When working at low levels, many factors such as contamination and substrate effects, which are otherwise of lesser concern, become critically important in influencing the reliability of environmental analyses. There is a growing awareness of the need to validate measurements and to be confident of their reliability and adequacy for environmental assessment. Consequently, national and international programmes of quality assurance are being recognized as essential requisites for satisfactory environmental data collection and are applied to sampling, sample preservation, preparation and analysis. Concerns include the choice of analytical method, the degree of accuracy required and the need for the exact identification of the contaminant, which may be difficult for contaminants such as oil and, even more so, for PCBs and some other organochlorine compounds.

For many contaminants, large-scale collaborative surveys have seldom been useful to establish spatial distributions of concentrations over large areas. International organizations such as the International Oceanographic Commission (IOC), United Nations Environment Programme (UNEP), International Atomic Energy

Agency (IAEA) and the International Council for the Exploration of the Sea (ICES) are actively engaged in inter-laboratory exercises to ensure more consistent and comparable results. The value of and necessity for these exercises have been well demonstrated, and it is recommended that they be continued and extended.

Inevitably, the poor comparability of earlier data limits their use. Often results have not been screened before being stored in data banks and the propagation and use of invalid data is a cause for serious concern. It is recommended that regional or global data banks should contain only validated data collected for a defined purpose, and that the purpose should be clearly stated. In all cases their quality should be indicated, and it should always be possible to link the recorded data with detailed information on methods of handling and analysis, quality assurance procedures and other information relevant to the assessment of data quality.

2.3.2 Concentrations in water

Open-ocean waters

Of the metals selected for review, mercury does not display any distinctive depth distribution in the oceans, at least on the basis of the data available. Measured concentrations in ocean waters range from 0.37 to 7.0 ng l^{-1}, although representative levels tend to be around 1 ng l^{-1}. In the north-west Atlantic concentrations are about twice those of the north-east Pacific, while in the western Pacific there is some evidence that mercury decreases along a north–south gradient, possibly as a result of atmospheric transport from the continents and deposition via rain. With regard to semi-enclosed areas, mercury concentrations in the North Sea and the Baltic Sea are similar to those in the north Atlantic; this may also be true of the Mediterranean, although reliable data are few.

For cadmium, reported concentrations in surface waters are more variable, from 0.2 to 200 ng l^{-1}. The lowest concentrations (up to 10 ng l^{-1}) are found in the open ocean, particularly in the sub-tropical and central gyres, with higher levels (up to 200 ng l^{-1}) in enclosed seas, such as the Baltic and the North Sea, enhanced by river inputs. River inputs are also proposed to explain a significant inshore–offshore gradient from 22 to 0.22 to ng l^{-1} in the north-west Atlantic, while in the north Pacific the higher inshore values are attributed to upwelling. Unlike mercury, cadmium shows a nutrient-like distribution, being low in surface waters and increasing with depth.

The concentrations of lead in the open north Atlantic and north Pacific oceans range from 5 to 50 ng l^{-1} in surface samples. Its vertical distribution – 8 to 10 times greater at the surface than in deeper layers – differs from that of cadmium, and is attributed mainly to atmospheric inputs arising from emissions from smelters and combustion of leaded petrol. These probably determine the latitudinal distribution, accounting for the three-fold higher levels in the north Atlantic compared with the north Pacific, and for the 8 to 10 times higher values in these northern areas compared with the south Pacific. There is some evidence that lead levels in the open north Atlantic are decreasing in response to a general reduction in the use of leaded petrol in North America over the last 10 years.

The available data for these metals suggest that mercury and cadmium in the open ocean are derived, for the most part, from natural sources such as rock weathering or sea-bed eruptions.

Arsenic is present in sea water principally as dissolved arsenate but also, in anoxic conditions, as arsenite. Concentrations in open waters surrounding the UK are around 2.6 µg l^{-1}. Lower values, 1.3 to 1.7 µg l^{-1}, are found in the Atlantic and 1.4 to 1.8 µg l^{-1} in the Pacific. Estuaries or inshore waters, especially in areas subject to mine drainage, may have much higher concentrations, 42 µg l^{-1} or even greater.

Selenium in ocean waters is about 0.1 µg l^{-1}, with higher levels in coastal waters, e.g. 0.2 µg l^{-1} in the Chesapeake Bay.

Chlorinated hydrocarbon levels in the open ocean are around a few ng l^{-1} and are fairly uniformly distributed at all depths, but the highest concentrations occur in surface microlayers naturally enriched in lipid compounds. Levels of PCBs in the surface waters of the temperate zone of the northern hemisphere reflect industrial use there and, in contrast to DDT, are higher than those in the tropics.

Some scattered data from the northern hemisphere show that toxaphenes – a collective name for chlorinated camphenes used extensively in some areas, mostly for the protection of cotton crops – are detectable in the marine environment.

Coastal waters

In coastal waters contaminant concentrations are largely associated with discharges to estuaries, but variability is high and dependent on the fluctuating physical and chemical conditions found in inshore waters. For mercury, values between 10 and 90 ng l^{-1} are recorded at hot spots, but may be only 1.0 ng l^{-1} or less close by, owing not only to the pattern of discharge, but also to the rapid formation and sedimentation of particulate forms of mercury.

Cadmium concentrations in coastal waters are determined by salinity, sediment load, nutrient chemistry and river discharges. Its distribution is complicated by abrupt changes in these factors in association with hydrographic fronts. Outside the influence of industrialized areas, concentrations in coastal waters range between 1 and 100 ng l^{-1}, in some cases reflecting geological sources which may mask the inputs of man-made sources, as for instance in estuaries in the south-west of the UK.

Similarly, lead is highest in the immediate vicinity of industrial activity and river inputs. For example in the southern Californian Bight measurements range from 25 to 150 ng l^-1, derived largely from sewage and storm run-off contaminated with lead from petrol. In coastal waters away from these hot spots, the major source of lead is the atmosphere, and levels do not differ significantly from those measured in the open sea.

Chlorinated hydrocarbons in coastal waters have their highest levels in industrialized zones, reaching 370 ng l^{-1} for PCBs in the Seine estuary, but values are usually much lower elsewhere, in the range 1 to 10 ng l^{-1}. DDT residues are generally below 5 ng l^{-1} in coastal waters, although, again, much higher levels have been reported near sources.

Coastal or semi-enclosed marine waters are characterized by enhanced levels of the nutrients nitrogen and phosphorus, as well as dissolved and particulate carbon. This contrasts with the levels of these nutrients in open oceans, which are usually close to levels of routine detection. Phosphorus occurs in both particulate and colloidal states, as well as dissolved as inorganic and organic phosphate compounds. Concentrations of phosphate in inshore waters range from 1 µg l^{-1} P/PO$_4$ in oligotrophic areas of the Mediterranean to about 10 µg l^{-1} in the eutrophic northern sector of the Adriatic. Levels of 20 to 30 µg l^{-1} are reported for the period 1980–84 in the Skagerrak.

Nitrogen occurs as dissolved inorganic nitrate, molecular nitrogen, nitrite and ammonium, and as organic nitrogen (e.g. urea, amino acids). Concentrations of nitrogen in the Mediterranean are reported as 14 µg l^{-1} N/NO$_3$ and in the northern Adriatic 70 µg l^{-1}. Values from 10 to 200 µg l^{-1} occur in the Skagerrak.

There is evidence from estimates of discharge loads, as well as from measured concentrations, that levels of nitrogen and phosphorus have risen in the past 20 to 30 years. In the Baltic Sea, for instance, discharge has increased by factors of four for nitrogen and eight for phosphorus, while sea-water concentrations have increased two- or three-fold for both. In the southern North Sea, both are considered to be about twice 'background' concentrations. The extent to which these concentrations will be reflected in open-ocean situations is determined by the physical diffusion and dilution of nutrients as well as by the uptake by organisms.

2.3.3   Concentrations in sediments

Contaminant concentrations in sediments reflect both local mineralogy and the nature and origin of the sediments (e.g. grain size, clay and organic content). Sediment heterogeneity and the large variations in measurements of contaminant concentrations in sediments make data interpretation difficult.

Information on deep-sea sediments is sparse but there also the range is considerable. Mercury measurements in sediments from the deep north Atlantic, for example, range from 0.01 to 0.6 ppm, although levels may be even higher in areas subject to volcanic or tectonic activity. Cadmium in deep-sea sediments is usually less than 0.5 ppm and lead ranges from 3 to 60 ppm. The data for chlorinated hydrocarbons in deep open ocean sediments are sparse, being apparently limited to samples taken during a series of cruises in the Mediterranean where values reported ranged from 0.6 to 8.9 ppb in 1975–7, and to a single core from the Sargasso Sea in 1974.

In coastal waters the data on sediments are more extensive but even more variable. Mercury concentrations span over three orders of magnitude from less than 0.01 ppm in non-contaminated areas to 5 to 25 ppm in heavily polluted embayments. The scatter of cadmium levels is as great, reaching, for example, a maximum of 140 ppm near a major sewage outfall close to Los Angeles. For lead, on the other hand, most measurements fall between 10 and 100 ppm. Levels of all these metals decline with distance from the coast, suggesting that elevated concentrations are generally derived from anthropogenic sources via rivers, run-off and sewage outfalls.

Arsenic concentrations in deep-sea sediments in the Pacific reach 20 ppm, with highest values closest to active volcanic ridges. Concentrations in inshore sediments are often lower, e.g. 14 ppm in Southampton Water and 3 to 15 ppm in Puget Sound. Much higher levels (50 to 300 ppm) occur in coastal waters receiving arsenic-contaminated effluents, or contaminated by deposits of arsenic-rich ores. Suspended particulate arsenic in the world oceans is 13 to 40 ppm dry weight.

Selenium is transferred from land sources to the ocean via rivers both in the suspended load and in solution. In the more alkaline waters of estuaries, insoluble selenite bound to particulate material predominates, but may subsequently desorb and become oxidized. A value of 0.15 ppm is typical of nearshore and shelf sediments.

Chlorinated hydrocarbons in nearshore surface sediments are well documented, and the highest levels are particularly associated with sewage discharges and industrial effluents, concentrations of 3200 ppb PCBs being measured in the Bay of Naples, declining to 10 to 30 ppb further offshore, while levels several orders of magnitude higher have been measured in Bedford Harbor, Mass, USA. When they can be dated with reasonable accuracy, some anoxic coastal sediment cores provide an historical record of metal and chlorinated hydrocarbon fluxes as a function of time.

While nitrogen is cycled effectively in the euphotic layer by biological activity, most of the phosphorus taken up in living organisms is sedimented out of the water column. Similarly, particulate carbon goes to sediments, which contain highest concentrations in the more productive inshore areas. Locations receiving sewage sludge or other organic solid wastes (e.g. pulp wastes) have particularly high levels of carbon, accompanied by a high Biochemical Oxygen Demand (BOD), which may restrict the suitability of these locations for stable benthic communities; initially, however, and around the edge of the sites, conditions may enhance productivity.

2.3.4   Concentrations in organisms

Mercury and cadmium have been measured extensively in mixed zooplankton samples from the Mediterranean, where concentrations are around 0.1 and 2 ppb, respectively. There mercury levels in krill (euphausiids) are similar to those in mixed zooplankton, but cadmium concentrations are much less. Benthopelagic oceanic rat-tail fish (*Coryphenoides armatus*) from the north Atlantic and the north Pacific have very similar levels of cadmium (0.025–0.027 ppm) and lead (0.012–0.016 ppm). For mercury, analyses of recently caught deep-sea fish compared with those of museum specimens collected in the 1880s suggest that no significant increase has taken place during the past century. Thus there is no evidence that the mercury found in deep-sea fish is related to human activities.

Arsenic is present in marine algae, typically at 10 to 100 ppm, about three orders of magnitude above levels in sea water. It is present in both water- and lipid-soluble forms and occurs as arsenobetaine in plankton and benthos, from which it is transferred via the food chain to molluscs (1 to 25 ppm wet weight) and shrimps (1 to 50 ppm wet weight) and eventually to man. In shrimps, much of the retained arsenic is in the exoskeleton, and is lost at moult. Pacific fish have 0.3 to 11.5 ppm wet weight and Atlantic fish 1 to 9 ppm. Data for marine birds and mammals are few, but shore birds have 0.01 to 1.5 ppm wet weight. Thus there is no evidence of biomagnification through the food chain.

Selenium displays behaviour similar to that of nutrients. It is selectively assimilated by phytoplankton and is further accumulated by marine organisms through food uptake. In uncontaminated areas, concentrations in molluscs are 0.4 ppm wet weight (*Mytilus*) and 3.5 ppm (*Ostrea*), and 0.2 to 2.2 ppm in crustaceans. Levels in fish are variable, 0.2 to 1 ppm wet weight, with large predators having concentrations as high as 4.3 ppm in muscle, and even higher in the liver (13.5 ppm). Marine mammals may also have high levels in livers, 46 to 400 ppm, but muscle tissue has much lower concentrations, about 0.5 ppm.

Data on chlorinated hydrocarbons in open-ocean plankton are sparse. In the case of PCBs, variability is high, concentrations in Atlantic samples being two orders of magnitude higher (about 400 ppb) than those in Pacific samples (less than 2 ppb) and almost an order of magnitude higher than in the Mediterranean (around 7 ppb). The Atlantic measurements, however, were made in the early 1970s and the reported levels may merely reflect the higher inputs into the waters that were prevalent in those years.

Observations on rat-tail fish collected at 3000 m depth in the north Atlantic show clearly that chlorinated hydrocarbons (PCBs, DDT and degradation products, but also HCH, toxaphene and chlordane) have reached the deep ocean, demonstrating transfer through food chains.

Concern has developed recently in Scandinavia and North America about the presence of chlorinated dibenzo-*p*-dioxins and dibenzo-*p*-furans in organisms living in the vicinity of pulp mill effluent discharges, especially in high-lipid tissues such as the hepatopancreas of crabs and the digestive glands of lobsters.

Fisheries have been recently closed off the west coast of Canada because of the presence of 2,3,7,8 tetrachlorodioxin and 2,3,7,8 tetrachlorodibenzofurans in edible fish.

Of great relevance to pollution impact are levels of contaminants in nearshore organisms more directly exposed to land-based sources and to higher water concentrations. Two monitoring strategies with different objectives have evolved. The primary aim of one is to protect human health, and it uses edible species of economic importance. The other strategy focusses on the use of comparable indicator species that are widely distributed and can thus be used to make assessments of space and time trends. The mussel *Mytilus* and related sessile bivalve species have received much attention for the latter purpose because they are ubiquitous or comparable, a common seafood item and they filter large volumes of water, concentrating contaminants from low ambient levels.

A worldwide review of measurements in mussels shows average values ranging from 0.1 to 0.4 ppm for mercury, 1 to 5 ppm for cadmium and 1 to 16 ppm for lead. Variability is high, however, particularly for mercury, and values as high as 7 ppm have been recorded in Adriatic specimens. In general, mercury levels in specimens from the northern shore of the Mediterranean are higher in mussels and in other marine organisms than in taxonomically similar specimens from the Atlantic, possibly reflecting natural mercury inputs of geological origin in the Mediterranean. Reliable data from other areas are sparse relative to those from the northern temperate latitudes.

2.3.5   Trends

Reliable geographical trends are extremely difficult to detect, given that so many intrinsic and external factors can affect measured concentrations, but some of the more comprehensive and long-term bivalve studies carried out in the northern hemisphere have proved useful, at least in connection with local sources of pollution. Thus, the US Mussel Watch Programme has, since the mid-1970s, detected hot spots of metal contamination. For example, bivalves from Hudson-Raritan Bay, Tampa Bay and Matagorda Bay are high in mercury, those from Copano, Delaware, Chesapeake and Hudson-Raritan Bays are relatively high in cadmium, and those from Hudson-Raritan Bay, Boston Harbor and San Pedro Bay reflect high ambient lead levels.

Time trends are even more difficult to establish because reliable records are not available for sufficiently long periods, or the same species has not been sampled consistently, although measurements in the Mississippi Delta sediments have shown systematic decreases of anthropogenic lead over the past few decades.

Marine organisms are also useful in pinpointing land-based sources of organochlorine pesticides and PCBs, particularly in the northern hemisphere. However, recent data on PCB and total DDT residue levels in mussels and oysters from various regions of the world show that the variability in all regions is large, often by up to three orders of magnitude. This fact alone severely limits intra- and inter-regional comparisons.

A striking feature of recent data is the continued widespread occurrence of DDT residues and PCBs in marine organisms. The highest values are found in organisms from areas with known industrial and agricultural inputs (e.g. Buzzards Bay and Bedford Harbor in the USA, the estuary of the St Lawrence in Canada and Osaka Harbour in Japan), and the lowest in organisms from less contaminated areas such as the Arabian Sea and the central coast of Brazil. Most of the data reviewed had been generated during the 1980s, i.e. long after restrictions had been placed on the use of DDT and PCBs in developed countries.

Although continued and consistent time series are difficult to obtain, a recent analysis of the results of different US monitoring programmes carried out through the 1970s to the 1980s provides some indication of trends. In the Southern California Bight, PCB levels in Dover sole (*Solea solea*) fell by more than an order of magnitude (from about 1 to 0.03 ppm) between 1972 and 1981. Likewise, levels in mussels near the Los Angeles County sewer outfall decreased 10-fold (from 2.5 to 0.24 ppm) between 1971 and 1978, but rose again to 0.56 ppm in 1979. An approximate and consistent three-fold decrease in PCBs between the mid-1970s and the early 1980s in samples of water, particulates and organisms from a single site in the north-western Mediterranean has been observed by the same analyst using the same method throughout the whole period of monitoring.

Convincing evidence of decline in the regional use of organochlorine compounds between the 1970s and the 1980s comes, for example, from studies of Arctic seals. In seals from the Canadian east coast DDT residues declined three- to five-fold between the early or mid-1970s and 1982, whereas PCBs fell by about half over the same interval. In Arctic ringed seals from the west coast of Canada, PCB levels declined by about the same factor. DDT levels, however, changed little during the same period, suggesting that continued use of the pesticide maintained an input to the western Arctic.

While the declining PCB levels are concurrent with the ban on the manufacture of these compounds in the early 1970s, DDT is likely to have been transported by the atmospheric route to the Arctic from parts of Asia where it is known to have been used extensively until at least the late 1970s.

2.3.6   Conclusions

Relative concentrations in different ecological compartments (water column, sediments, organisms) are valuable in developing models of transfer from source to target, in establishing spatial and temporal trends and possibly in identifying a mechanism for toxic action. Analyses of environmental samples are often used in monitoring programmes to signal contamination by potentially hazardous agents. It must be emphasized, however, that these data, in themselves, do not demonstrate adverse effects. Indeed, high concentrations may indicate only a chemical sequestration. In some cases, data on concentrations can be misleading. For instance, discharges of nutrients may be quickly taken up by plankton, and thus seen as increased production, not as higher concentrations in water. Again, some toxic agents may operate at low concentrations by triggering an effect, without being de-graded or bound up in the process, so that measurements of their concentration do not provide a true indication of their impact.

The few exceptional data sets that do allow some estimate of temporal trends in coastal areas are long-term analyses of organ-isms and of marine sediment cores. The Mussel Watch and other similar projects in North America and Europe show recent de-creases in chlorinated hydrocarbons in organisms from highly contaminated coastal locations where contaminant inputs have been reduced (e.g. Hudson-Raritan Bay, Los Angeles Bight, Baltic Sea). With the possible exception of those for lead, no similarly reliable, validated, data sets make possible the assessment of temporal trends in the water column.

The inherent difficulties in achieving reliable results from ana-lysing trace contaminants in sea water, coupled with the fact that their concentrations are transient, severely limit the use of sea water for monitoring contaminant trends. On the other hand, sediments and organisms, generally good integrators of contami-nant inputs, are easier to analyse for trace contaminants and offer the best way at present to establish spatial and temporal trends in contaminant distribution.

Bearing in mind these reservations, the interpretation of data on contaminant concentrations should always be cautious. It must be guided by an understanding of transfer processes and supported by plausible mechanisms of toxicity. Monitoring programmes generate their own momentum, and periodic critical review is needed to ensure priority of effort and resources. To develop the basis for analysis of geographic and temporal trends, analytical data must be subjected to quality control procedures with an assurance that methods of sampling and analysis provide sufficient intercomparability. International programmes provide a good basis for this and should be encouraged; the UNEP Regional Seas programme, the IOC/GEEP programme and the Mussel Watch are examples.

Chapter 3

Biological Effects

This chapter discusses some of the most critical topics for the assessment of the state of marine ecosystems and of human health in relation to the marine environment. A brief reference is also made to biological data quality assurance as was done earlier (Section 2.3.1) in the field of chemical analysis, for which the needs for quality control, data validation and good management are better recognized. There are comparable needs in biological studies but rigorous quality control is often not sufficiently practised.

3.1 Human Health Effects

Although the sea provides an important source of human food and an attractive environment for recreation, sea water contains a wide variety of agents, biological as well as organic and inorganic, all of which can be a hazard to human health. Use of the sea and its living resources determines the extent to which health is affected.

Rapidly expanding and, in many cases, seasonally increased coastal communities and discharges from rivers draining agricultural and industrial areas are the prime source of anthropogenic contaminants in the nearshore marine environment. The principal problem for human health on a worldwide scale is the existence of pathogenic organisms discharged with domestic sewage to coastal waters, estuaries or rivers and drainage canals that carry these organisms to the sea.

Bathing in waters receiving such inputs and consumption of contaminated fish and shellfish are the causes of a variety of infections. Chemical contamination of sea water is also a potential threat to human health, while tainting and spoilage of seafood is of economic concern. It should be emphasized, however, that the problems are not entirely man-made. Naturally occurring aquatic biotoxins are also a health hazard, particularly in the tropical and sub-tropical waters of the Pacific and Caribbean Regions.

Several bacteria (e.g. halophilic vibrios) pathogenic to man are indigenous to estuarine and sea waters. Man is also exposed to parasitoses from the consumption of fish infested by worms such as *Anisakis* that have a complex life cycle through marine mammals and sea birds.

3.1.1   Microbial agents

These can affect human health as a consequence of sea bathing or consumption of seafood. The impact on health during bathing and related recreational beach activities arises from two broadly classified cause/effect mechanisms:

- Contact with microbially polluted sea water which may result in ear, eye and skin infections or respiratory diseases. Micro-organisms such as *Staphylococcus aureus* or *Pseudomonas aeruginosa*, as well as certain viruses, are held responsible for such infections, which may be associated with high bather densities. Halophilic vibrios can also cause ear and wound infections.
- Ingestion of sea water contaminated with pathogens from domestic sewage. The consequences may be diseases or disorders caused by bacterial or viral pathogens excreted through the human gastro-intestinal tract. Since it is usually difficult to establish the aetiology of such disorders, indicator organisms such as faecal coliforms and enterococci are used to estimate contamination by pathogens. Most of the diseases associated with the ingestion of enteric pathogens affect the gastro-intestinal tract, but some are respiratory in their effects or involve other body systems.

Gastro-intestinal infection due to swimming in sewage-polluted sea water is the most widespread health effect in estuarine and other coastal areas with high population densities. Seasonal population increases at tourist resorts add considerably to the problem, causing increased sewage influx as well as much higher exposure rates due to crowding. As visitors may have low levels of immunity to the local endemic diseases they are especially susceptible. Recent epidemiological studies in the USA and in the Mediterranean have cast a new light on the causal relationship between bathing in sea water contaminated with pathogens of faecal origin and disease among the bathers. The relationship is particularly strong in the case of children under five.

Earlier views, that there is no demonstrable causal link between human disease and bathing in contaminated sea water, can no longer be supported. There is thus a good case for establishing microbial standards for bathing areas, based on faecal indicator bacteria. However, recent observations have shown that the incidence of bathing-related gastro-intestinal diseases is much better correlated with *Enterococcus* than with *Escherichia coli* counts, and is not correlated with total faecal coliform counts.

The same urban sewage which leads to bathing problems is also often responsible for acute gastro-intestinal disorders following the consumption of contaminated seafood. Molluscs and other seafoods are particularly susceptible to contamination by pathogens carried to sea in wastewater flows, since their growing sites are often in highly polluted areas near urban centres. More important, bivalves filter large volumes of sea water and retain pathogenic bacteria and viruses. The fact that these shellfish are popularly eaten raw or only partially cooked greatly increases their disease-causing potential. The 1973 cholera epidemic in Naples, Italy, was initiated by contaminated molluscs. Infectious hepatitis is the most important viral infection transmitted by seafood, and numerous outbreaks of hepatitis demonstrate that molluscs grown in sewage-contaminated water are very effective carriers of the viruses.

The prevalence of these infections is largely determined by cultural habits governing the consumption of shellfish. Gastro-intestinal infections and cases of diarrhoea and viral hepatitis have been reported from much of the West African coastline, the Asian seas, the Pacific and the Caribbean. Many investigations have shown high counts of indicator organisms (total and faecal coliforms) as well as of bacterial and viral pathogens in sea water, in bivalves and in sediments.

Massive outbreaks of infectious hepatitis and cholera associated with the consumption of raw shellfish harvested from wastewater-polluted coastal areas have brought public attention to this problem. Strict standards for shellfish and shellfish-growing waters have now been widely established, but only a small fraction of the incidents are reported.

Recent studies suggest that, even inland, a substantial proportion of all cases of endemic infectious hepatitis is associated with the consumption of raw bivalves including, in some cases, those harvested under what are currently considered acceptable sanitary conditions. An investigation in one European country has detected a high level of enteric virus contamination in shellfish samples from a major urban market. The new findings raise important questions about the adequacy of current shellfish sanitary practices, including handling and storage, and point to the need for a careful re-evaluation of existing standards and regulations.

In conclusion, the present state of knowledge indicates that the most clearly identified health risk associated with coastal marine pollution by urban wastewater is the transmission of disease by the consumption of raw shellfish harvested in contaminated areas. Monitoring and control of the wholesomeness of marketable shellfish should therefore be further strengthened, effective depuration methods employed consistently, the conditions of shellfish beds supervised more effectively and beds exposed to sewage-contaminated waters excluded from harvesting.

3.1.2 Chemical contaminants

Chemicals with a potential to cause harm to human health if ingested with seafood are present naturally in sea water and their concentrations can be increased by man's activities. Natural levels in sea water are usually low (mostly $ng\ l^{-1}$), but the relatively elevated concentrations of mercury ($\mu g\ l^{-1}$) in predatory fish in the Mediterranean and in the Seychelles Islands, and of cadmium in crabs from the Orkney Islands off Scotland and copper in the estuarine fauna of Cornwall are striking examples of geologically associated contamination. Studies in these regions have shown that, although exposure levels are much higher than elsewhere, no clinical effects have been detected among consumers. In general, the risk from exposure to naturally occurring chemicals is considered to be low.

Anthropogenic inputs of chemical contaminants, mainly originating from industrial discharges to estuaries or coastal waters, can result in locally much higher concentrations and correspondingly more severe potential and actual health effects. The case of mercury-polluted effluents from an industrial plant at Minamata Bay, where contaminated seafood was a major component of the local diet from the opening of the plant in the 1930s until 1968, is an alarming example of such health risks. Medium- or long-term exposure to chemicals in seafood may cause a variety of health effects, depending on the chemical agent, the amounts ingested and the total body burden resulting from all routes of intake.

A variety of chemicals is involved. Synthetic organic compounds or mixtures, such as PCBs, accumulate in sediments or are associated with detritus and can be taken up into the food chain and recycled years after the input has ceased. In some areas, such as parts of the middle Atlantic Bight of the USA, fish consumption has been restricted because of the high levels of PCBs in the flesh (e.g. up to 84 ppm in lobsters and 730 ppm wet weight in fin fish in the Bedford Harbor area) and high levels were maintained even after PCB releases had been curtailed. Petroleum is a widespread potential contaminant but the strong flavour usually present in oil-tainted seafood is a deterrent to consumption and thus a protection of public health. Heavy metals are widely perceived as being of concern, and edible fish and shellfish are regularly monitored by some countries in this context. Concentration limits set internationally through the FAO/WHO *Codex Alimentarius* and also by many national food inspection services protect the consumer, and overt health effects have been confined to exceptional events, such as at Minamata.

3.1.3   Aquatic biotoxins

Various toxic substances are produced by many phytoplankton species. Until about a decade ago the organisms known to be implicated were mainly pelagic dinoflagellates, chiefly of the genus *Gonyaulax*, both paralytic and diarrhoeic shellfish poisoning (PSP and DSP) being caused by consumption of bivalve molluscs that have accumulated toxins from these dinoflagellates. Phytoplankton blooms producing such shellfish toxins are documented as annual events in many parts of the world.

Saxitoxin and related toxins which cause PSP usually have little effect on shellfish but are potent neurotoxins to vertebrates, including man, causing respiratory paralysis and death by asphyxia. PSP was recorded in Canada as long ago as 1793 and over the past 20 years has become common throughout the world. Between 1969 and 1983, 905 cases were documented, with 24 deaths. PSP is now being reported much more widely. In 1983, for example, PSP was recorded for the first time in the Philippines. It resulted in 21 deaths along with 300 cases of illness, and a ban extending for 18 months was imposed on the harvesting and sale of shellfish. Countries with a long history of PSP (such as Canada, the USA and several states bordering the North Sea) have developed regular monitoring programmes to ensure public safety, causing minimum disruption to shellfish harvesting.

DSP has been recognized only more recently, but it also affects both cultivated and wild shellfish in many countries. The contamination of shellfish with diarrhoeic toxins (okadaic acid, dinophysistoxins and pectenotoxins) causes severe gastro-intestinal disturbances but no fatalities have been reported. The dinoflagellates responsible can contaminate shellfish at low cell densities, well below those which alter the colour of the water, so phytoplankton monitoring is necessary.

Dinoflagellates that produce ciguatoxins contaminate a variety of tropical and subtropical grazing fish, particularly in the southeast Asian seas and the Pacific, where the human disease ciguatera, characterized by neurological, cardio-vascular and gastro-intestinal symptoms, has emerged as a major constraint to fisheries development. Human exposure occurs through eating predator fish that feed on the grazers. As many as 50 000 individuals may be poisoned annually, with fatality rates from 0.1 to 4.5%. Temperate countries are involved through imports of tropical fish. The annual cost to fisheries in Florida, the Caribbean and Hawaii from lost business, exclusive of legal actions, is estimated at US$ 10 million. Approximately 2300 cases occur in the USA and Canada each year, costing up to US$ 20 million, mainly due to time off work and hospitalization. No effective monitoring programme has yet been developed.

Apart from dinoflagellates, other flagellate groups, often small species in the size range 10–20 µm have recently been implicated in toxic episodes, and major problems are reported in both brackish and sea water, particularly from Israel and Japan. The full extent of the threat from aquatic biotoxins is not at present well understood and the possibility of encountering unexpected situations or even new biotoxins is well illustrated by a recent event in Canada.

This concerned an outbreak of shellfish poisoning resulting from the consumption of blue mussels contaminated with the neurotoxin domoic acid produced by the diatom *Nitzschia pungens*. It is referred to as amnesic shellfish poisoning and caused neurological symptoms, including memory loss, and human fatalities, and led to the closure of shellfish beds. While a particular concern at the time was that the production of domoic acid was previously unknown, subsequent work suggests that this toxin is a relatively common product of *Nitzschia pungens* but was detected only when the incident of acute shellfish poisoning occurred in 1987.

3.1.4   Conclusions

Cases and outbreaks of gastro-enteric diseases occur in Europe and North and South America, but the tropical and sub-tropical waters of South and East Asia and the Pacific are the main foci of these public health hazards. The other beach-linked diseases, however, are common to all crowded beaches, especially those exposed to nearby sewage discharges. Successful breaking of the faecal–oral transmission route must include the control of sewage and pathogen discharges to coastal waters or, in the short term, restrictions on the use of polluted beaches and in the consumption of contaminated seafood. Much remains to be done in this respect, particularly in the densely populated developing countries bordering the tropical and sub-tropical seas.

For toxic blooms not obviously connected with sewage, or even with eutrophication, careful monitoring and public awareness are required, and a better understanding of the relevant food chains and associated conditions is needed.

Except for examples of massive contamination as at Minamata, current levels of toxic chemicals in seafood do not appear to be a major source of hazard to man, and there are national control measures aimed at excluding chemically contaminated food in general from the market. Monitoring of edible fish should, however, be continued as long as chemicals are released to the marine environment. Surveillance for the presence of marine biotoxins, on the other hand, will be a never-ending obligation.

3.2   *Biological Significance of Environmental Concentrations*

Levels of common contaminants in water, sediments and the tissues of living organisms have been reviewed in Section 2.3. The significance of these concentrations for marine species and communities is discussed here. The effects of nutrients are considered in Section 3.3.

The effects of present concentrations of contaminants can be considered in terms of exposure to materials dissolved in the water column or deposited in sediments, or as tissue concentrations. The nature and form of a contaminant and its behaviour determine its biological action: most analyses refer only to 'total' or 'extractable' constituents, and the results may be misleading as a guide to possible effects. 'Acute', i.e. short-term, effects on individuals have also to be distinguished from longer-term re-

sponses of affected species or populations. A further consideration is whether the human use of a marine resource is affected;
this may have serious economic consequences for the value of a
commercial species.

3.2.1   Trace elements

Among metal contaminants, mercury presents a special case
because of the conversion of inorganic forms of mercury to persistent organic forms and their subsequent concentration through
food chain transfers to top predators, with accumulation in fatty
tissues over their longer life span.

Zooplankton and benthic molluscs can accumulate both inorganic and organic mercury, the former with quite rapid turnover,
the latter much more slowly. These classes of organisms, and
fish, take up mercury from sea water, rather than sediments, at
rates proportional to concentration. Levels in sea water below ng
l^{-1} appear to have no effect on algae or zooplankton in the water
column. Inorganic mercury is taken up by phytoplankton only by
passive diffusion, and is rapidly eliminated. Long-lived ocean
fish have high levels of mercury in muscle, but fish in enclosed
seas or coastal waters may have residues up to a thousand times
higher. These high muscle concentrations are predominantly of
natural origin, as a consequence of net accumulation through a
long life history. There is no evidence that these accumulated
residues have produced any effect on fish.

Predators of fish, such as sea birds and mammals, accumulate
organic (methyl) mercury in tissues to exceed those of fish, those
feeding inshore having higher levels than those feeding in open
oceans. There is little evidence that high tissue concentrations (in
livers or feathers of sea birds) are damaging, possibly because of
an associated and antagonistic uptake of selenium. However,
declining numbers of fish-eating ospreys and sea eagles have
been associated with tissue levels of up to 50 ppm.

At Minamata, Japan, mercury poisoning from the consumption (20–50 μg day^{-1}) of locally contaminated seafood caused
2000 cases of intoxication between 1930 and 1968, with 43 deaths
recorded from 1953. That disaster led to the adoption of recommended international limits for levels of mercury intake in the
diet (0.3 μg week^{-1} of total mercury) and for seafood concentrations.

There is disputed evidence of accumulation of cadmium in marine waters through the food chain, although it is evidently taken

up by phytoplankton. Zooplankton and filter feeders dependent on phytoplankton have body burdens of a few ppm but some oceanic fish have only 0.03 ppm (dry). Although cadmium is not considered an essential element, concentrations up to 100 μg l^{-1} have enhanced phytoplankton growth in laboratory experiments. No effects are reported for algae, molluscs and crustaceans with levels of 0.4 μg l^{-1} in sea water. These 'no effect' levels are significantly higher than general background levels in ocean or coastal waters (about 0.001 to 0.2 μg l^{-1}), but may be exceeded in some inshore areas.

There appears to be little direct accumulation of cadmium from sediments by benthic organisms, and it is generally thought to be taken up from water. Cadmium is transferred from marine algae to molluscan herbivores and through them to predatory carnivores where it is sequestered as metallothionein (e.g. in molluscan kidney tissues, or fish liver and gills).

Marine organisms take up lead from sediments or inshore waters with high inorganic lead concentrations; uptake by mussels appears to be linear with time of exposure. Like cadmium, low levels of lead (800 μg l^{-1}) enhance growth of some phytoplankton species, possibly in response to accompanying nitrate anions; in other species no effects were found at 100 μg l^{-1}. Adverse (growth) effects are reported at 300 μg l^{-1} for some protozoa, and 100 μg l^{-1} produced total mortality of the crustacean *Gammarus locusta*. Acute mortality of molluscan embryos occurs at 500 μg l^{-1} but adults are more resistant with sub-lethal effects occurring at higher concentrations. These 'effect levels' are orders of magnitude higher than sea-water concentrations (less than 0.01 μg l^{-1}). There have been cases of lead poisoning of aquatic birds feeding in sea and fresh water but in general lead contamination of the sea and of marine organisms is not a matter of concern. Although lead intake through human diet contributes a possibly significant fraction to the human body burden, that associated with marine products is not considered significant.

The acute toxicity level (LC_{50}) of arsenic for various mollusc species is 350 to 750 μg l^{-1}, but abnormal development in some bivalve and crab species is reported at 200 to 300 μg l^{-1}. Acute effects in marine mammals generally are found only at about 10000 μg l^{-1}. Even at the highest levels in sea water reported, arsenic seems to pose no major threat to marine organisms or man.

A strong correlation is observed between selenium and mercury concentrations in seals and fish, and the approximately equimolar ratio of the two metals observed in marine mammals has suggested a Hg/Se structural or biochemical relationship. Correlation of selenium with other metals in invertebrates is also reported. Algae appear not to be sensitive to selenite at concentrations lower than 80 μg l^{-1}. Other marine species are unlikely to be affected unless concentrations exceed 100 μg l^{-1}, at least a thousand times higher than typical sea-water concentrations. Thus, no risk is apparent for marine organisms, even in contaminated waters.

3.2.2 Halogenated hydrocarbons

Toxic effects of halogenated hydrocarbons can be seen at most levels in the food chain: in laboratory experiments, primary productivity is reduced by 50% at only 1 μg l^{-1} concentrations in sea water but such effects have not been detected in the sea, where open-ocean concentrations are several orders of magnitude lower. The shrimp *Crangon* shows 50% mortality at 1 to 100 μg l^{-1}, and fish (various species) are affected at similar concentrations in sea water; the Baltic flounder (*Platichthys flesus*) has reduced egg hatch with ovary residues of only 120 ppb. Bivalves concentrate contaminated particulates and have high body burdens but their populations appear to be unaffected.

Seals and sea birds in some areas of the Baltic have high tissue residues of organochlorine compounds and are harmed as a consequence. There has been a sharp decline in birds of prey, while fish-eating birds have reduced egg hatch at high body burdens (up to 900 ppm in liver). Many seals in the Baltic and the Dutch Wadden Sea have been found dead, some with uterine occlusions associated with PCB blubber levels of up to 110 ppm. Seals from the Farne Islands, however, thrive even with residues of 122 ppm. Blubber from seals in northern temperate seas has up to 190 ppm and 100 ppm (dry) of PCB and DDT, respectively; residues in seal blubber from southern oceans are much lower.

3.2.3 Petroleum hydrocarbons

Hydrocarbons from oil exploitation and use are present in the open North Sea at concentrations of 1 to 3 μg l^{-1} and at lower concentrations in the open ocean. Levels of hydrocarbons an order of magnitude higher occur close to oil platforms and in estuaries with significant shipping, offloading and refining activities. Sediments have 5 to 160 ppm, but this may rise to more than 1000 ppm in polluted estuaries. Effects reported on living organisms near oil rigs or accident spill sites include high tissue levels of induced enzyme activity (e.g. mixed function oxidase) in molluscs, reduced growth in sea grass, behavioural change and recruitment failure in crabs, and successional changes in small benthic crustaceans. Higher oil residues have also been reported in the livers of fish. A sea-water concentration of 50 µg l^{-1} of the aromatic fraction of oil, compared with the natural background of only 1 µg l^{-1}, would need to persist over a wide area before significantly affecting the larval stages of fish.

3.2.4   Conclusions

This brief review shows that, with the possible exception of mercury, trace metals are present in such low dissolved concentrations in ocean waters and even in most coastal waters that they do not constitute a hazard to marine organisms. The accumulation of organic mercury residues is associated with damage to fish-eating birds, and the risk of mercury poisoning of man justifies control measures to limit the dietary intake through seafood. It is not known, however, precisely how sea-water concentrations relate to mercury levels in fish. Cadmium, although included among the 'black list' substances controlled by international agreement because of its possible effects on man, appears to present no hazard to marine organisms or to man via seafood. Similarly, arsenic accumulated by marine organisms appears to have no adverse effects at present levels.

Halogenated hydrocarbons pose a demonstrable hazard to top predators which accumulate residues in fatty tissues; the risk is more significant where such organisms are living near hot spots of contamination, such as sewage dump sites and industrial discharges. Oil, while a significant pollutant affecting amenity when present as slicks or tar balls, seems otherwise not to pose a serious hazard for marine organisms, except at the site of oil spills, or of continuous releases from refineries and at other industrial sites. However, some habitats, particularly in polar regions and in the tropics, are particularly vulnerable and in enclosed coastal waters even spills of around 100 tonnes have caused great damage to sensitive species, such as marine birds and mammals.

Within the marine ecosystem, many natural and man-made factors interact in a complex way. A number of approaches have been developed to provide some measure of the total effect of these conditions on biological targets. Among the physiological responses to adverse conditions are anomalies of growth, fecundity and development; biochemical indices have also been used. The limitations, as well as the strength, of such an integrated approach need to be taken into account. In particular, the almost total lack of a baseline for many biological properties is a serious deficiency. None the less it is important to recognize the need to specify the factor(s) contributing to damage, so that remedial action can be focussed in the most effective way on the factor(s) found to be critical.

In recent collaboratives exercises, IOC/GEEP has successfully conducted parallel observations of ambient conditions, physiological and biochemical reactions at species level, and population and community responses. This approach is now being applied in the tropical environment by a similar exercise.

This review has revealed the inadequacy of our knowledge on the relationships between sea-water levels and their ultimate effects on organisms and man. Since these relationships provide the only sound biological basis for the derivation of environmental standards, co-ordinated research on a whole range of contaminants and organisms is urgently needed.

3.3 Eutrophication

In freshwater lakes the impacts of unnaturally large additions of nutrients are well known – changes in primary production and species composition, intense algal blooms and generally deleterious effects, such as oxygen depletion, with consequent effects on water quality and living resources. For some time, similar events were thought to be unlikely in the marine environment which, being larger and more dynamic, would have the capacity to absorb nutrient inputs. It is recognized, however, that enhanced productivity does occur naturally in the sea, for example as a result of upwelling and seasonal river discharges or land run-off. None the less there is evidence of increased frequency and scale of exceptional algal blooms in the sea in recent years at the same time as nutrient inputs have increased.

The rate of primary production in the sea is limited by a number of factors including the availability of nutrients and certain trace substances, light, temperature, water column stability and such biological factors as grazing pressure and the presence of a suitable seed population of phytoplankton. However, the maximum size of the crop is usually critically determined by the availability of nutrients such as phosphorus and nitrogen compounds. While phosphate has, in certain areas (e.g. in the Adriatic), been shown to be the growth-limiting nutrient in the sea, inorganic nitrogen compounds usually play this role, in contrast to the situation in fresh waters where phosphates are the major factor. Nitrogenous nutrients are introduced to the sea by plant and animal decomposition, animal excretion and also by air–sea exchange and oceanic mixing processes. Human activities add to all of these processes. The most common land-based sources of nutrients are domestic wastes (principally sewage), agricultural run-off of excess fertilizers, animal wastes from intensive live-stock units, aquaculture, certain types of industrial effluents and atmospheric deposition.

Globally, present inputs of nutrients from rivers due to man's activities are at least as great as those from natural processes. The inputs in different localities vary widely, depending on a range of factors including population density, land use, effluent treatment, estuarine topography, dispersal rates and natural marine sources of the nutrients. In some enclosed waters and coastal seas these inputs have led to clearly detectable and sustained increases in nutrient concentrations in the water. The areas thus affected are numerous and geographically widespread but all have the common feature of limited water exchange with the open sea.

There is no evidence of comparable sustained increases in open-shelf waters or open-ocean areas and there seems little likelihood that this could occur with the present rate of inputs since 80 to 90% of the nutrient input is taken up by primary production within estuarine and nearshore waters (see Chapter 2). A significant observable effect of excessive nutrient inputs can therefore be expected inshore, and this is indeed manifest in the frequent occurrence of algal blooms and the increased biomass of benthic algae and aquatic vascular plants. Limited increases may have desirable consequences in terms of enhanced production, but large inputs will degrade the environment in a number of ways, especially if the oxygen demand of the decaying plant material from large blooms leads to hypoxia and the death of sensitive organisms with high oxygen requirement, such as fish.

In the Baltic Sea, systematic monitoring since 1980 has produced evidence of eutrophication, as seen in progressively decreasing oxygen concentrations and increasing levels of nutrients. Recorded biological effects over the same period indicate higher summer rates of primary production and, since 1980, of increased productivity, including that of fish, but exceptional and unwelcome blooms of plankton algae have also occurred. Although it is recognized that some events are related to climatological and hydrological variations in the Baltic, the documented increases in nutrient inputs to this enclosed sea are a matter of major concern.

Possibly related to higher nutrient inputs was the unusual bloom that occurred along the coasts of Denmark, Norway and Sweden in 1988. The algae responsible was the small flagellate *Chrysochromulina polylepis* which reached maximum concentrations of 50–100 million cells per litre. The bloom did great damage to seaweeds, invertebrates and fish in coastal waters between 0 and 12 m depth along a 200 km stretch, and, through an unidentified toxin, also affected farmed salmon, costing the Norwegian fishing industry over US$ 10 million. Although the toxin does not accumulate in fish flesh, it has been found in blue mussels (*Mytilus edulis*) but there were no reports of illnesses in man. The remarkable feature was that this species had not been recorded previously as producing large blooms in these waters and was not known to be toxic.

Off the Dutch coast nitrogen in sea water increased by a factor of four and phosphorus by a factor of two over the period from 1930 to 1980. In the inshore waters of the German Bight the increases were by factors of 1.7 and 1.5, respectively, over 23 years. Phytoplankton biomass increased dramatically during the same period and flagellates overtook diatoms in abundance in the planktonic community. Nutrient flux, rather than concentrations, appears to be the forcing factor.

The coastal areas of the southern North Sea have very high winter levels of nutrients and correspondingly high primary production in the spring, with notable seasonal changes in phytoplankton species composition. Macrobenthos mortality due to oxygen deficiency has occurred in the past and more extensively in recent years. The northern Adriatic also shows signs of eutrophication as a result of high inputs of nutrients through rivers and coastal developments. This has been associated with seasonal occurrences of algal blooms and, in limited areas, with anoxic conditions, sometimes resulting in mass mortalities of fish and benthic invertebrates in shallow waters. In the summer of 1988, possibly owing to the climatic conditions (exceptionally calm, hot weather) prevailing in that year, an unusual proliferation of algae released vast amounts of slimy material that fouled beaches along both the Italian and the Yugoslav coasts.

The Inland Sea and other sea areas of Japan have serious problems with excess nutrients, mariculture being particularly affected through the impact of phytoplankton blooms. In the New York Bight, anaerobic conditions resulting in fish kills are attributed to some combination of eutrophication and weather conditions. These examples indicate widespread adverse effects of high levels of nutrient additions, although toxic blooms also occur without obvious eutrophication. The areas affected have restricted water exchange and anoxic conditions are common to them all. Toxic blooms or changes in fisheries yield are recorded in many of them.

It is now possible to recognize the sequence of changes that characterizes progressive stages of eutrophication in the sea. An idealized progression of phenomena is

(a) enhanced primary production,
(b) changes in plant species composition,
(c) very dense blooms, often toxic,
(d) anoxic conditions,
(e) adverse effects on fish and invertebrates,
(f) impact on amenity,
(g) changes in structure of benthic communities.

Not all these features are observed in every case and the full sequence is not always obvious. Indeed, changes in the structure of benthic communities are often the earliest signs of eutrophication, probably because the benthos integrates the exposure over time. The effects of concern to man are reduced fisheries yields or gross fish kills, and amenity deterioration with attendant economic losses. More directly, health risks result from exposure to flagellate neurotoxins passed through shellfish. Recognition of this sequence may make remedial action possible at a sufficiently early stage to avoid serious consequences.

Relevant long-term and episodic events can be monitored through measurements of

(a) turbidity,
(b) oxygen concentrations,
(c) nutrient concentrations,
(d) phytoplankton chlorophyll and
(e) macrophyte and benthic fauna biomass and diversity.

Satellite observations are often informative, especially for charting the scale, development and decay of blooms. At present, modelling and conceptual frameworks seem more likely to be useful heuristic tools rather than accurate predictive instruments, but this may change as our understanding develops.

Experience has shown that it is possible to control and reverse eutrophication by reducing discharge of nutrients and organic carbon. There are well-documented cases of recovery of fishing grounds damaged by nutrients from sewage sludge after dumping has stopped. For specific point sources, it can be sufficient to discharge effluent further offshore to an area of greater water movement, since adverse enrichment is less likely if the nutrients are adequately diluted and dispersed. In areas with restricted circulation, removal or diversion of a substantial part of the nutrient load (particularly nitrogen) and its release to suitable areas should be considered. Effective techniques are available for nutrient stripping but the costs are high and, where the main source of nutrients is agriculture, major changes in farming procedures or intensity would be entailed for effective reduction of discharges.

When interpreting data on eutrophication and forecasting effects, it must be recognized that the marine environment shows ill-understood short-term fluctuations and even less well-understood long-term changes due to natural causes. Moreover, it is difficult to predict effects in large geographical areas to which a variety of sources provide inputs, each of which by itself might not be significant, but which together might have a cumulative effect on extensive areas such as the New York Bight, the Baltic Sea or the coastal zone of the south-eastern North Sea. However, it should be possible, at least on a local scale, to identify areas of restricted water exchange such as lagoons, inlets, fjords and enclosed bays which, if subject to enhanced nutrient input, might be expected to show adverse effects, and to afford these areas a greater degree of protection or control.

3.4　Ecological Effects

3.4.1　General considerations

Long-term effects of contaminant exposure of populations or communities are difficult to distinguish from natural changes. Reliable observations of population changes over sufficient time (decades) are largely limited to some commercial species, ocean plankton and a few inshore benthos communities. Statistical analysis of the data is not always convincing. In addition, the cause of the change is not always recognized and it needs to be supported by realistic laboratory and field experiments. This may leave a trend, even though statistically established, 'looking for a cause'.

The establishment of a relationship between a toxic agent and the frequency or intensity of effects on a target requires that the dose and the mode of exposure be defined and that this be interpreted in terms of wild populations rather than of individuals used in laboratory or field toxicity testing. The effects of exposure will vary not only between different pollutants (or mixtures) and the conditions of exposure (continuous or intermittent) but also between different species or strains, and stages in the life history. Thus, population exposure must be related to the spatial and temporal distribution of pollutants and target organisms as well as to within-species reactions.

A few substances may be instantly lethal in trace quantities, but such substances are uncommon and their dangers are soon recognized. It follows that we are concerned more with exposure over the long term, either continuous or intermittent, and with delayed or subtle effects, especially those that are reflected by anomalies in recruitment (i.e. population replacement by reproduction and/or immigration) or competitive interactions within or between species in the community.

Many experiments rely on measuring short-term responses to relatively high concentrations of single pollutants and a limited set of associated exposure conditions. To translate this in realistic terms usually calls for an extrapolation of the response to lower concentrations and over life-time exposures. These approaches may be frustrated if there is an unknown threshold of effect, as for substances essential at low concentration, or where environmental conditions (such as temperature or pH) play a significant role.

Response commonly varies between individuals according to age, sex, size, physiological state and genetic make-up. The spatial and temporal distribution of a contaminant in the environment also may not be known, nor its precise relation to the location and exposure of the target population. Further, for highly mobile organisms such as fish or marine mammals, the past history of exposure is usually not known, and reliance is placed on the accumulated residues (body burden) of a suspected toxic agent. This strategy is dependent on the degree to which toxic agents are persistent and on knowledge of their accumulation in tissues, as well as on the age, food-chain relationships and past exposure of the target organisms.

If toxicity or process studies are to be extrapolated to the population level, sufficient understanding of the population structure of target species is necessary. This requires the application of general concepts of population or community response to experimental exposure, often of single species, to contaminants. However, this goal is likley to be unrealistic for more than a handful of species of commercial or conservation interest, and for only a few contaminants.

Given this diversity of conditions in the real environment, and the difficulty of predicting the biological response of communities from laboratory or even field tests on limited samples of a few species, the value of toxicity studies lies more in revealing potential mechanisms of response and establishing thresholds of acute (lethal) effect. None the less, such studies do help the interpretation of phenomena in the field, and often provide a plausible explanation of the observed damage.

A further problem arises in that contaminants in polluted and coastal waters do not occur in isolation, but as complex and varying mixtures and along with changing environmental characteristics. Changes in temperature, dissolved oxygen and suspended sediment loads are often significant determinants of chemical form and availability, so that biological response is modulated by interactions between contaminants and natural variables, as well as by biological factors.

If a population does decline, relaxation of interspecific competition leads to a changed community, in the first instance by a localized change in species dominance or loss. This will be irreversible if recruitment from adjacent populations cannot occur. The time-scale of recovery and the degree to which population changes can be reversed and species or communities restored are uncertain since they are critically dependent on the specific conditions at the damaged site, as well as on the potential for replacement. The study of these conditions along concentration gradients from point sources of a pollutant and following accidental releases, as well as the subsequent recovery of damaged habitats and communities, is of considerable practical value.

The difficulty of monitoring biological change, given its long-term and extensive geographic variation, and the problem of interpreting these observations in the light of the results of experimental exposures of a few species to a few known contaminants, are not easily resolved. Where changes are expected, for example in areas receiving discharges, monitoring programmes may be initiated, but they may involve an expensive and long-term commitment of resources, often unpopular with funding agencies, control authorities and even with scientists. In addition, it is often charged that irreversible damage will ensue before the results of long-term programmes are accumulated and analysed.

It follows that long-term field observations seldom provide early warning of significant effects at population level, nor do they by themselves identify the principal or even important causative agents. Aside from catastrophic events, it is usually difficult to distinguish between natural and man-made causes of biological change. The careful analysis of natural phenomena (e.g. El Niño), or of changes in biological communities following accidents or along a gradient from a pollutant source seems to offer the best direct evidence for population response to natural events or human activities. These field investigations can be enhanced by studies of biological and chemical mechanisms and processes, and by the development of models of extrapolate relevant findings to populations. An indirect assessment may be made from the combination of

(a) data on population dynamics,
(b) process studies of contaminant impact and
(c) knowledge of spatial and temporal distribution of the contaminant.

To illustrate the problems inherent in the detection of long-term effects at low concentrations of contaminants, or where a suspected cause has not been identified, a variety of examples of biological change attributed to natural phenomena and/or to human activities are given in the following section.

3.4.2   Case histories

Population changes

A survey of the plankton community in the North Atlantic and the North Sea since 1948 provides a 40-year record of geographical, seasonal and year-to-year changes and makes it possible to judge whether there have been community or productivity changes over time. A convincing relationship of phyto- and zooplankton changes with the occurrence of westerly weather, and with sea-surface temperature in the months from February to

June, emerges. This is statistically sufficient to relate the apparent long-term and persistent decline in the zooplankton record up to 1980 to natural phenomena, so that the presence of unidentified low-level contamination need not be invoked. Data on levels of contaminants in the ocean waters over the period of the plankton observations are largely lacking, however, and so the question of possible pollutant effects is unresolved, although the possible adverse influence of some man-made trace chemicals such as PAH has been proposed in some oceans and enclosed seas.

A further well-documented example of biological change is that of the 'Russell Cycle'. In this case, a long-standing investigation of water quality conditions in the Western Approaches to the English Channel has been matched by systematic biological ob- servations of plankton and fish larvae. The study began in the 1920s, when the major fishery of the regional ports was for her- ring (*Clupea harengus*); at that time one of the indicator zooplank- ton organisms was the arrow worm, *Sagitta elegans*. In later decades the herring fishery declined, to be replaced by pilchards (*Sardinia pilchardus*), and the zooplankton indicator became *S. setosa*. At the time, specific pollutants were not identified although phosphate levels, measured routinely, were used as an important indicator of productivity. After some decades the situation re- versed, and herring larvae were found again in the plankton. The variable then most closely correlated with community change was found to be sea temperature, associated, again, with a long-term cycle of westerly winds controlling the influx of warmer Gulf Stream water into the coastal waters off south-west Britain. This temperature effect altered the boundary between Channel and North Atlantic fauna sufficiently to create a major shift in species at the sampling station off Plymouth. So, although during the initial studies it was thought that water quality was the key, and routine water quality observations were undertaken throughout the period of observation, it now seems that the most probable explanation lies in changes in external and natural phenomena triggering the shift between the two faunal complexes.

For a number of commercially exploited fish species there is a sufficiently long record of their populations from which to judge the possible effects of pollutants or of exploitation. Older catch records go back to the 15th century, well before any significant pollution. In the case of the Atlantic cod (*Gadus morrhua*), increased catches were seen in warmer climatic periods in the North Atlan- tic when, through the 1920s, sea temperatures rose by more than 1°C. Among pelagic herring species, notable fluctuations in stock size have been evident in the Hokkaido herring, the North Sea herring, the Bohuslan herring and the California herring and sardine. Whereas the Bohusland (Baltic) herring shows a periodicity of about 110 years, and alternates with that of the North Sea spring-spawning herring, all the other stocks show similar patterns of good and bad years. In the case of the North Sea herring, these reflect the periodicity of ice cover north of Iceland. Similarly timed changes in the widely separate stocks of Adriatic, Californian and Japanese sardine are considered indicative of widespread climatic change. A shorter-term cycle is that of the Peruvian anchovy, which is influenced by the oscillation of hydrographic conditions known as El Niño (see Section 1.10.1). This regular reduction of coastal upwelling in the eastern Pacific leads to reduced productivity and to a limited distribution of the anchovy, which remains abundant only in areas where productivity is maintained.

Temperature effects

Temperature produces significant direct and indirect effects at all levels of biological organization. Point-source discharges at higher than ambient temperature, in contrast, are almost entirely local in their effect. A long-term (25 years) study of effects on the benthic fauna adjacent to a thermal discharge from a 2000 MW nuclear power plant (Clyde estuary, UK) has demonstrated fluctuations in growth and abundance of the principal macro- and meiobenthic species, attributable to both climatic and thermal effluent influences on recruitment, growth and mortality. In some years, a higher than average recruitment to the population was associated with higher than normal temperatures prior to spatfall. The fluctuations, however, appear to have had little effect on the rather stable benthic community. Another long-term analysis of recruitment of juveniles to the population of an inshore fish (sand melt, *Atherina presbyter*) in an enclosed bay (Southampton Water) showed no change in population structure over a 12-year period of thermal discharge from a 2000 MW fossil-fuel power plant. Thus, although strictly local and short-term effects of such point source discharges can be identified, it is difficult to distinguish natural fluctuations from those due to human activities. A worldwide warming as a result of a change in climate might, however, have more significant effects in the marine environment, e.g. by changing the extent of habitats as a result of a sea-level rise, by favouring species with higher temperature tolerance or by increasing the rate of critical physiological processes.

Changes in coral reefs

Oil spills, disruptive fishing practices, mining, development impacts and storms are obvious causes of damage to coral reefs. Changes inland (deforestation) have also been correlated with reduced coral reef cover in the Pacific, because of increased sediment load in the run-off waters, which is damaging to corals. There have also been reports of at least localized decline, with 'bleaching' due to the loss of zooxanthellae from the tissues, attributed to various contaminants (e.g. the herbicide, 2,4 D, oil, sewage, nutrients) but often without critical evidence or testing. A recent report argues that the loss of zooxanthellae is associated with meteorological and oceanographic events which have resulted in marked increases in surface-water temperatures in extensive areas. In this case, natural cycles of change could again be held responsible.

In the Indian and Pacific Oceans, however, the major cause of damage to coral reefs is now the predation pressure from the crown-of-thorns starfish (*Acanthaster planci*) which exhibited massive population increases in the years 1968 to 1972. The extent to which the increase is related to human activities is unknown.

Decline in marine mammals

The accumulation by marine mammals of lipid-soluble toxic chemicals, such as chlorinated hydrocarbons, from transfer through the food chain, has raised concern that adverse effects would follow. There is indeed evidence from areas of the Baltic and Wadden Seas that PCB residues are responsible for sterility among common seals (*Phoca vitulina*). However, although concentrations of PCBs in common seals and killer whales (*Orcinus orca*) in Puget Sound are among the highest in the world, no correlation has been found there between birth rate and presence or concentration of contaminants.

It is now generally accepted that the deaths, in 1988, of thousands of seals in northern European waters (Baltic, North and Irish Seas) were caused by a previously unknown morbillivirus, phocine distemper virus. Since PCBs and other associated compounds such as chlorinated dioxins and dibenzofurans appear to depress the immune system in mammals, it has been suggested that seals might have been weakened by exposure to these substances. However, deaths were not concentrated in the most highly polluted waters in the affected area, nor have the seal tissues shown unusually high concentrations of PCBs or pesticide residues. The part played by contaminants in the epidemic, therefore, remains uncertain.

Fish diseases

Many externally visible diseases are prevalent in fish populations, and their incidence has been proposed as an index of pollution, either on the basis that toxic agents are present in the water, or that general unfavourable conditions (low oxygen, high temperature) are found. The association of fish diseases with pollution, however, requires consideration of their natural incidence and variation in relation to season and geographic area as well as water quality, and to fish species, age, condition and population density. Sufficient evidence is not yet available on the level of most diseases studied, nor on the influence of specific pollutants.

None the less, the 'wastewater burden' has been linked with a high frequency (20 to 30% of all fish sampled) of some diseases of various aetiology in dab, *Limanda limanda*, in polluted areas of the German Bight, and a high occurrence of lymphocystis, ulcers and fin rot is reported for flounder, *Platichthys flesus*, caught in waters off the Netherland coast. Similar evidence has been put forward for other sea areas, notably Puget Sound. Some take the view that the circumstantial evidence in some areas is sufficient to link the occurrence of fish diseases with water pollution. Others, however, consider that the relationship is still uncertain. Further investigations are now in hand, including specific disease identification, experimental exposure to suspected agents, and more intensive field surveys to clarify the relationships and provide a baseline of incidence of various diseases. This work should be encouraged.

Beached sea birds

Sea birds are exposed to contaminants in the sea through predation on contaminated marine organisms or by direct contact with oil residues or plastic debris on the sea surface. A survey of beached sea birds is maintained in some areas to monitor the effects of man-induced hazards. In the autumn of 1969, a massive disaster affected birds in the area of the Irish Sea, with more than 12000 birds cast up on the adjacent shores. Almost all those affected were adult guillemots (*Uria aalge*) just past the moult. Efforts were made at the time to assess the possible influence of epidemic disease, lack of food or accumulation of pollutants. No clear conclusion could be drawn, though the effects of exposure to pollutants, including PCB residues, could not be ruled out at that time.

3.5 Recovery of Damaged Ecosystems and Species

It is pertinent to consider the extent to which damaged habitats and species are able to recover once polluting inputs have ceased. An ecosystem damaged by oil, nutrients or sewage will typically have lower species diversity, shorter food chains and less efficient energy transfer between trophic levels than an unaffected ecosystem. The simplest expectation is that the pre-impact system will eventually be re-established. However, since ecosystems are highly dynamic, often with several possible stable states, recovery need not follow the same sequence or time scale as loss, and the system will not necessarily revert to its previous structure.

The effects, and also the recovery, will depend on local conditions. Wastewater discharges, even if they do not carry toxic chemicals, may still result in an overall increase of nutrients as well as in a change in their balance. For example, municipal wastewater discharge around Stockholm has greatly increased in quantity since the beginning of the century, adding in particular to the phosphorus loading of the receiving waters and resulting in heavy blooms of nitrogen-fixing blue-green algae, decreased water transparency and periods of oxygen deficiency with hydrogen sulphide generation. Between 1968 and 1973, biological and chemical purification was introduced to all sewage treatment plants in Stockholm and, as a result, the phosphorus concentration in surface water dropped from 17 to 4 $\mu g \, l^{-1}$, the frequency of occurrence of blue greens decreased, water transparency improved, oxygen content is increasing and free hydrogen sulphide is now seldom found.

As another example, the River Thames in the UK was rich in fish centuries ago, but increasing sewage load and other discharges through the 19th century caused substantial reductions in dissolved oxygen. By the early 1950s, several miles of the tidal waterway were oxygen-deficient every summer, long stretches were without fish life and the bottom fauna was dominated by tubificid worms. The modernization and enlargement of two sewage treatment plants and the improvement and curtailment of industrial discharges resulted in greatly enhanced water quality. The oxygen content of the receiving water increased and general conditions improved; about 100 fish species are now present and whiting (*Merlangius merlangus*) and smelt (*Osmerus eperlanus*) have returned; gravid shrimps are found, and the estuarine communities of macroalgae, benthic macro-invertebrates and wildfowl have become more diverse. In 1983, following the earlier introduction of juveniles upstream, immigration of adult salmon to the Thames was re-established, and the first salmon (*Salmo salar*) in 130 years caught by rod and line was recorded.

In the nearshore waters of southern California municipal sewage is a major input. In 1971 Orange County diverted its marine outfall from a position at around 18 m depth to a deeper one further offshore at 53 to 60 m. Prior to the change, the benthos close to the outfall was dominated by a few species of small, opportunistic polychaete worms and the fish fauna was sparse. Within three months of the discharge terminating, organic carbon and sulphide concentrations in the sediments had returned to background levels with significant increases in the diversity of fish and benthos and the disappearance of the previous dominants. Many further examples show that the adverse ecosystem changes resulting from nutrient enrichment by sewage both in the water column and in the sediment are reversible, sometimes very rapidly.

Wastes from the pulp and paper industry constitute another polluting input with high oxygen demand. A 25-year investigation at a plant near Fort William in western Scotland measured greatly enhanced organic carbon inputs over a 4-year period. A four-fold rise in benthic faunal biomass early in the operation was followed by a dramatic decline after discharge ceased. Such enrichment of the benthos is often characteristic of the initial effects of eutrophication. Further organic sedimentation may lead to progressive bottom-water anoxia with reduction or even elimination of benthos. This is evident also in an area of the Baltic where pulp- and paper-mill wastes have resulted in anaerobic zones of a few square kilometres. Improved water treatment procedures have reduced the oxygen demand and the bulk of wood fibre discharge by more than 90%, and these anaerobic zones have now been eliminated in the Baltic.

With mercury pollution, the pattern of events is different. In Sweden, phenylmercury was used as a slimicide in the pulp and paper industry until it was banned in 1968. Before the installation of treatment to remove suspended material from the wastewater, fibre banks contaminated by mercury were allowed to accumulate in the receiving environment. Phenylmercury in these banks is gradually converted to inorganic mercury and then biologically methylated to forms that leach out and are taken up by aquatic organisms. Along the Swedish coast of the Baltic, mercury-contaminated fibre banks remain and, since the rate of methylation is low, will provide a low-level but persistent source of mercury to the marine environment for the foreseeable future. One approach to recovery is removal of the offending deposit, and this has been done in some Swedish bays. In one area, 15 000 dry tonnes of deposit were removed by a suction dredger and subjected to wastewater treatment. This removed 99% of the total mercury from the bay, with the result that methyl mercury levels in pike (*Esox lucius*) dropped significantly and a ban on fishing was lifted.

Once the environmental dangers of DDT and PCB were discovered, their use was restricted or banned in many northern hemisphere countries in the early 1970s. Subsequently, levels in the environment dropped, for example, in areas off the Californian coast, in Japan's Inland Sea and in the Baltic. After a few years, concentrations in living organisms also declined, and PCB levels in Baltic seals dropped by 50%. Since then, however, there has been no evidence of further decrease, and adverse effects remain. In the case of DDT, total residue levels (consisting mainly of DDE) declined from the early 1970s and, by 1984, were only 10% of the earlier levels. However, residue levels increased again after 1984, and the egg shells of fish-eating birds, which had begun to return to normal, have recently become thinner again. Thus, while the bans and restrictions produced an initial decrease of these synthetic organics, the downward trend has now halted, possibly because past contamination built up persistent residues in sediments, from which they are now steadily recycled.

The best documented record of ecosystem recovery is that from oil incidents, although the extent and speed of recovery varies considerably. In some cases large spills seem to have had only minor impacts, while in others small quantities of oil have caused considerable damage. Apart from any clean-up treatment applied, many factors are relevant, including the nature of the oil, the meteorological conditions, the season, the characteristics of the affected area, and the opportunities for recolonization. In general, pelagic systems in the open sea are not seriously affected and recovery is a matter of weeks or a few months. The effects on sub-tidal communities are more extreme and recovery takes longer; in intertidal areas where the oil may have been buried in the sediment and can leach out over a long period, recovery has taken decades.

Experience has been gained on the re-establishment of some important tropical and sub-tropical habitats – coral reefs, mangroves and sea-grass beds. In some cases these habitats have been destroyed by physical activities such as port developments, bridge building or by destructive coral mining and fishing, as well as by thermal discharges and natural storm events. Corals are notably slow to recover from damage. Only a few per cent of a reef is regenerated each year and a badly damaged reef may take several decades to recover. On the other hand, some studies show up to 80% recovery of mangroves in a year, and techniques have been developed for replanting, usually successful where competitive vegetation is restricted in the conditions of variable salinity and tidal height in which mangroves thrive. Sea-grass beds have also been restored within a few months by replanting, and their associated epifauna recovered within the same period. However, successful recolonization and re-establishment will occur only if the degraded environmental conditions that induced the original problem are corrected.

As a result of the relative frequency of major oil spills in recent years and the study of their consequences, our understanding of the effects of oil on many ecosystems has advanced greatly. Comparable opportunistic studies of other types of polluting events should be encouraged.

3.6   Quality Control of Biological Data

The need for quality assurance, data validation and management in chemical studies has been reviewed in Section 2.3. There is a parallel and equally important need for similar quality control of biological data. However, as biological measurements are more diverse and inherently more variable than chemical measurements, it is more difficult to distinguish errors due to sampling from those due to analytical procedures. Some biological methods are well standardized, but others rather idiosyncratic.

In spite of promotion of standard methods, or nationally or internationally agreed procedures, individual laboratories often follow methods of their own choice. In addition, the inherent variability of populations and communities leads to a diversity of techniques and many biological data are 'snapshots' of dynamic and variable parameters rather than determinations aimed at absolute, or even relative, values of stable characteristics. This makes comparison between different data sets difficult, unless comparable methods have been used and statistical limits to the estimates obtained. A defined procedure should always be maintained throughout a long-running investigation, and sufficient observations be made to obtain the desired levels of significance.

At a stage where it is necessary to look for relationships between environmental factors and biological responses, this lack of systematic quality control for the biological components of an investigation is inconsistent with the critical scrutiny given to chemical observations, and detracts from the value of the derived relationships. Major efforts are needed to improve this situation.

The collection of biological material for analysis of contaminant content is rarely undertaken with sufficient safeguards to ensure that the samples are representative of the population. Some programmes have adopted indicator species as standard test organisms, but this is itself constrained by the limited distributions of species, which are seldom global.

The accurate identification of species is still a significant problem in some biological samples, and there are contentious attributions and difficulties. Steps should therefore be taken to provide training opportunities for taxonomists, particularly in developing countries, where specialists are few and much of the highly diverse marine flora and fauna is not described.

While biological data can never attain the accuracy of chemical analysis, improvements could result from the promotion and support of further collaborative studies. Some progress has already been made at both national and international level with acceptance of robust and reliable, as well as widely available, methods of sampling. Joint biological investigations which parallel to some degree the interlaboratory exercises conducted for chemical analysis, for instance the activities promoted by IOC/GEEP, should be strongly encouraged.

Chapter 4

Climate Change Effects

4.1 General Considerations

The increase of atmospheric CO_2 from the burning of fossil fuels and the increase of other greenhouse gases have raised concern about the possibility of induced climate variations during the next decades and about their associated impacts. Substantial scientific research is now being directed towards assessing the extent and nature of these climate changes. The current authoritative review on these matters is the Report of the 1985 International Conference on the Assessment of the Role of Carbon Dioxide and of other Greenhouse Gases in Climate Variations and Associated Impacts, usually referred to as the Villach Report. Its conclusions are being reviewed by a UNEP/WMO Intergovernmental Panel on Climate Change.

The report states that the global amounts of carbon dioxide, chlorofluorocarbons, methane and nitrous oxide have been increasing. These gases, usually referred to as greenhouse gases, are all transparent to incoming short-wave radiation, but absorb and emit long-wave radiation, and their increased concentrations can lead to a warming of the Earth's surface and of the lower atmosphere. The report concludes that it is necessary to study separately the effects of each of these gases in order to estimate their relative contributions to the warming at any given time. So far, the main effort has been devoted to CO_2. However, because the atmospheric concentrations of other greenhouse gases are increasing much faster, their relative impact on climate change will soon approach that of CO_2, if present trends continue. For CO_2 the reserves of fossil fuel are large enough for climatic changes due to increased CO_2 levels to occur if these reserves continue to be exploited at a high rate in the future.

Atmospheric CO_2 has been rising at the rate of about 1 ppmv (parts per million per volume) per year starting at 315 ppmv in 1958 when good measurements became available. Uncertainty regarding the future increase of atmospheric CO_2 centres not only on how much CO_2 will be released from fossil fuel combustion (about 5 Gt C y^{-1} in 1980) but also on how much will be taken up by the oceans (estimated at 2–3 Gt C y^{-1}) and released by biomass destruction – primarily deforestation. At present the atmospheric load of CO_2 is increasing by about 2.5 Gt C y^{-1}.

It has generally been agreed that neither regional patterns of climate change nor the ways in which higher CO_2 concentrations and the attendant changes in climate would affect ecosystems and human activities can yet be predicted.

It is important to note that climate models indicate that the increase in global mean equilibrium surface temperature due to increases of CO_2 and other greenhouse gases equivalent to a doubling of the atmosphere CO_2 concentration is likely to be in the range of 1.5–4.5°C, most plausibly in the lower half of this range. However, the observed increase in global mean temperature of 0.3–0.7°C over the last hundred years cannot be ascribed in a rigorous manner to increasing concentration of CO_2 and other greenhouse gases, although the magnitude is within the range of predictions.

The global sea level is estimated to have risen some 12 cm during the 20th century. On the basis of the observed changes since the beginning of this century, it is forecast that a global warming of 1.5–4.5°C will cause the mean sea level to rise by 20–140 cm. The major contributing factor to such a rise would be the thermal expansion of ocean water. The range of the estimates is an indication of their uncertainties.

Extensive research, much of it carried out within the World Climate Research Programme (WCRP), aims to predict climate changes from natural and man-made causes over the shorter (several years) and the longer term (several decades). The research effort for the assessment of the shorter-term changes is concentrated in the tropical regions where inter-annual variations are evident in both the oceans and atmosphere, and where well-known phenomena such as El Niño have major environmental impacts. International research within the WCRP is centred on the Tropical Ocean and Global Atmosphere Programme (TOGA), which focusses on the coupled response of the large-scale atmosphere with the tropical ocean.

Climate prediction on decadal time scales is limited by the inability to describe and model the circulation of the world ocean on this scale. The WCRP has therefore organized the World Ocean Circulation Experiment (WOCE) to design a research programme to develop models useful for predicting climate change and to collect the data necessary to test them. In the longer term, a second goal is to find methods for monitoring the long-term changes in the ocean circulation.

WOCE will collect global data sets, including measurements of sea-surface temperature and altimetry; the distributions of heat; the horizontal velocity field at one deep level at least, as measured by floats; and the surface fluxes of momentum, heat and water as obtained from a number of satellite-based and *in situ* measurements combined with the analysis of atmospheric general circulation models. The programme also includes a number of experiments aimed at making it possible to characterize those processes that are important for predicting decadal climate changes. These experiments will be concentrated in the Atlantic Ocean. The WOCE Intensive Observation Period is planned for 1990–95 and the programme is now entering its implementation phase.

The question of the uptake of anthropogenic CO_2 in the ocean has been examined by the Committee of Climate Change and the Ocean (CCCO), and a global programme has been proposed to measure the concentration of oceanic dissolved inorganic carbon, alkalinity and/or pH, and to detect changes in this concentration over time scales of a decade or so. Samples will be collected during WOCE.

The overall problem of the oceanic carbon cycle and its role in climate change is the subject of the Joint Global Ocean Flux Study (JGOFS), whose main goal is to determine and understand on a global scale the processes controlling the time-varying fluxes of carbon and associated biogenic elements in the ocean, and to evaluate the related exchanges with the atmosphere, sea floor and continental boundaries. The scientific programme for JGOFS is only now being developed. It is giving special importance to studies of CO_2 and the need for global satellite observations, especially of ocean colour.

As the greenhouse gases accumulate in the atmosphere, the changing climate will probably alter the rate at which the oceans take up CO_2. But at present we cannot say whether the net effect of this feedback will increase or decrease atmospheric CO_2 and affect the magnitude of the associated climate changes.

Potentially important interactions may modify climate changes. The timing and distribution of plankton productivity and the species responsible for it will change with climate. Since the CO_2 flux from air to sea is at any point controlled in part by the net productivity occurring there, these biological changes may also engender a change in the CO_2 level. On the other hand, some authors have suggested that increased organic carbon flux off the continental shelves due to the greater supply of nutrients now reaching shelf seas may constitute a sink of fossil-fuel carbon dioxide. If this is the case, then the eutrophication discussed in Chapter 3 may counter to some extent the CO_2 increase through increased algal uptake.

The background concentration of CO_2 in the atmosphere is not constant. Studies of air trapped in ice cores from Greenland and Antarctica have shown that it has changed in a regular pattern over at least the last several hundred thousand years and that it correlates closely with the cycle of the ice ages. Rapid natural shifts in CO_2 and climate have sometimes occurred in periods of a few centuries only, and have prompted the view that the natural system may be highly non-linear and may tend to flip between stable states rather than evolve gradually. The theoretical possibility exists that man's activities may trigger such a reorganization of the natural system.

The depletion of stratospheric ozone observed over Antarctica during the Austral spring, attributed to increasing atmospheric concentrations of chlorofluorocarbons, is another reason for concern. Beside altering the radiative balance of the Earth and thus contributing to changes in climate, such depletion leads to enhanced UV-B fluxes in the surface layers of the southern oceans during the spring phytoplankton blooming. The potential exists for this to affect the marine ecosystem adversely, in particular via the primary producers which must photosynthesize in the euphotic zone. However, these effects will be difficult to monitor and demonstrate because of the magnitude of the changes and the natural variability of the ecosystem.

4.2 Sea-surface Temperature

As mentioned previously, the Villach Report has predicted changes of global mean equilibrium surface temperature in the range of 1.5–4.5°C as the result of the doubling of greenhouse gases that may take place in the next decades. It is expected that there will be wide variations of this temperature change with latitude. In particular, the amplitude of the changes in the tropics is predicted to be small with larger changes at mid-latitudes and still larger effects at the poles. In addition, it is predicted that at mid-latitudes there will be a change of the mean with an annual cycle similar to that found at present. In contrast, at the poles the summer-time temperature is expected to remain similar to that currently observed, close to the freezing point of ice, while in the winter large increases in temperature are anticipated.

Changes in ocean temperature as a result of this general global warming are most difficult to predict. These will arise not only from changes in the local air temperature and radiation balance, but also from differences in the ocean circulation due to changes in the large-scale forcing of the ocean by the atmospheric winds and the surface fluxes of heat and water. Thus, the ocean circulation as well as the way it transports heat may change substantially. It is worth noting that the direction of the net meridional heat flux is unknown in some ocean basins. Improving knowledge in this regard is one of the main goals of WOCE but great progress towards providing reliable estimates before the end of the century is unlikely.

Some indication of the complexity of the expected changes in ocean climate can be seen from the results of global coupled ocean/atmosphere circulation models. These models are limited by computer power, have poor horizontal oceanic resolution and use simplified physics for a number of ill-understood processes. Even with these limitations, initial results show that, in spite of the general atmospheric warming, the ocean may actually become cooler in some high-latitude regions due to upwelling of deeper cold water.

Although within the next few years global climate change predictions will improve, regional climate patterns will not be forecast successfully for a long time. In contrast, robust estimates of ocean-temperature change will probably be obtained initially for regional basins, where the change will arise primarily from changes in the radiation balance and the temperature of the nearby land masses.

For the present, studies of the effects on the marine environment of changing ocean temperature due to the increase of greenhouse gases will be limited to the 'what if' scenarios. These can be used to consider the sensitivity of the local marine environment to changes in temperature and circulation within some range of values that may not yet be well determined.

4.3   Sea-level Rise

One of the problems facing the prediction of sea-level change is that the historical record is far from clear. Although there is sufficient observational evidence to support the 'accepted' global sea-level rise over the past century, the mechanisms responsible for this rise are not well understood.

Primary mechanisms include increases in oceanic volume due to the melting of small glaciers and/or thermal expansion of the upper ocean, vertical glacio-isostatic rebound of the lithosphere in response to deglaciation and tectonic deformation of the crust due to plate motion. Tide gauge data from regions of relatively stable tectonics and uniform isostatic rebounds have led some authors to attribute changes in sea level to thermal expansion and glacial melting. Whether or not this might be related to oceanic warming due to increases in atmospheric CO_2 concentration is not clear.

It is difficult to separate short-term from long-term changes in relative mean sea level. Experiments are now being planned using the power of absolute positioning systems borne on satellites to measure the changes in tide gauge stations relative to a fixed global co-ordinate system, allowing the determination of sea-level changes. However, data for this purpose will not generally be available for some time.

Predicting changes in sea level is complicated for many of the same reasons that cause difficulties in predicting changes in ocean temperature. Since the major contribution to sea-level change is expected to be the thermal expansion of sea water, a basic element of any prediction is the change of temperature with depth. Although models will predict sea-level changes as a function of position and time, these will be most difficult to verify.

Meanwhile, as for ocean temperature, environmental effects of changing sea level can best be estimated using the range of sea-level values given in the Villach Report. Over the next few years these estimates will be refined, especially their geographical distribution.

4.4   Environmental Impacts

The uncertainty of sea level and oceanic temperature changes make assessments of the magnitude of the environmental effects highly speculative. Some potential consequences can, however, be identified.

Half the world's population dwells in coastal regions which are already under great demographic pressure and are exposed to pollution, flooding, land subsidence and compaction and to the effects of upland water diversion. A rise in sea level would have its most severe effects in low-lying coastal regions, beaches and wetlands. In developed countries protection for some regions will be possible, whereas in developing countries without adequate technical and capital resources it may not be. The frequency and severity of flooding would increase, and coastal structures and port facilities would require reinforcement. A number of Pacific and Indian ocean islands with a maximum altitude of a few metres are especially vulnerable and could become uninhabitable after rises of the sea level that would hardly be noticed elsewhere.

Natural wetlands, of great value as nursery grounds for many commercial fish species, as habitats for wildlife and as zones of coastal protection, are already under pressure worldwide. They may be unable to extend landward and might be lost or undergo substantial changes. Salt-water intrusion would occur in some drainage and irrigation systems, groundwater, rivers and bays.

Marine ecosystems could be affected by increased temperatures and alterations in coastal circulation patterns, as well as by changed water stratification due to increased run-off following greater precipitation. In polar regions, pack-ice conditions could be greatly changed, leaving some areas of the Arctic ice-free. This would reduce the albedo and lead to local warming, affecting the ecosystem as a whole.

Chapter 5

Prevention and Control of Marine Pollution

5.1 Basic Concepts

It is obvious that pollution should be prevented or controlled, but it is not always clear how much effort and financial resources are justified, what time scale is appropriate, and what mechanisms are most effective. Problems arise in particular when:

- there is insufficient basic scientific knowledge of toxic agents, targets or dose-response relationships;
- there is inadequate technology available to achieve satisfactory control or prevention;
- there is restriction of resources needed to take a preferred option;
- there is little experience of consequences of alternative options (of production or disposal);
- there is an evident cost of the proposed action but the expected benefit cannot be valued.

None the less, consensus among nations, particularly when there is an underlying conviction that 'something must be done', has led to effective action being taken. However, debate continues between those calling for a total ban of the offending activity, or 'zero' discharge regardless of costs, and those seeking to improve the control of discharges to the environment of potentially harmful substances. The pragmatist would favour a solution that is effective even if not absolute, rather than one that in practice is difficult to implement.

Over the past century, there has been a gradual development of practical control strategies, at national and international level. The preferred approach varies with the circumstances of the case, and each has its advantages and disadvantages, as reviewed below. These approaches, however, have many aspects in common and all have the objective of reducing pollution in an effective and economic way.

The environmental (or receiving, absorptive or assimilative) capacity (EC) is defined as a property of the environment which measures its ability to accommodate a particular activity, or rate of activity, without unacceptable impact. The capacity is finite and quantifiable for any particular site, expected contaminant input and activity range, on the basis of physical, chemical and biological characteristics. The notion of EC forms the basis of a variety of practical measures commonly adopted for the control and prevention of pollution.

A set of principles with an important bearing on this subject has also been elaborated by the International Commission on Radiological Protection (ICRP). These principles, which are relevant to regulating any of man's activities that may have an impact upon the environment or human health, are as follows.

- *Justification.* No practice should be adopted unless there exist clear net benefits to society, i.e. the overall benefits outweigh the overall detriments to the society affected. Justification applies to an entire practice (e.g. the production, use and fate of a new agricultural pesticide) and not only to individual components of that practice, such as the disposal of any waste products;
- *Compliance with exposure limits.* Limits of exposure to products, their raw materials and associated wastes by both employees in relevant industries and members of the public should be established and observed.
- *Optimization.* Exposures to the substances concerned should be kept as low as reasonably achievable, taking technical, social and economic factors into account. Thus, exposures should be reduced by technical means, or through the use of alternative options for the handling and disposal of products and wastes, so that the overall exposures resulting from the activity are as low as economically and socially justifiable. The application of this principle requires complex balancing of scientific, economic, social and political factors, but in many cases these balances can be somewhat simplified.

A further concept relevant to pollution is that of 'sustainable development', as recently outlined in the Report of the World Commission on Environment and Development (the Brundtland

Report). This approach is proposed to permit advance or expansion of human communities without detriment to the human condition. The underlying principle of sustainable development is that the exploitation of resources, the direction of investment, the orientation of technological development and institutional change should be consistent with future as well as with present needs. The profligate use of environmental resources should no longer be acceptable and action is needed to make economic growth compatible with an acceptable environment.

5.2 Prevention and Control Strategies

Each of the pollution control approaches adopted by countries for the implementation of international conventions has its merits, but none provides on its own a fully workable basis for action. Conflicts between these approaches sometimes arise, and are not resolved by insistence on the superiority of any particular one. Any move towards a comprehensive international strategy must recognize the strengths and weaknesses of each national approach, and the possible relationship to the policies of the different countries.

5.2.1 Environmental quality objectives (EQOs)

Environmental quality objectives define some desired state of the environment that can be met through the attainment of specific targets, such as the maintenance of salmon migration through an estuary, the production of uncontaminated seafood or the preservation of beach amenity. The use of an EQO requires the establishment of appropriate environmental quality standards, and the application of these standards in turn demands extensive knowledge of, for instance, dose–response relationships, and relies on comprehensive programmes for monitoring the condition of the sea. In principle, such standards take into account the input to the sea from all sources, including non-point sources, for example from the atmosphere. In practice, for large water bodies with a variety of individual sources it will be hard to assess the contributions of each and then to control or regulate the discharge. When environmental levels in a given area approach limiting quality standards, it becomes difficult to determine the remaining environmental capacity that could be allocated to proposed additional discharges to that area.

5.2.2   Uniform emission standards (UESs)

Emission or source standards, and the limit values associated with them, may control point sources effectively, but they cannot deal with non-point source inputs such as agricultural run-off or atmospheric deposition. By definition, they apply to individual, not to multiple sources. As these standards are based on the 'best practicable' or 'best available' technology, there is the problem of determining these and of adjusting the respective standards to changing technology. As so far developed, emission standards are generally formulated on the basis of the hazardous properties of particular chemicals, rather than on specific environmental damage.

5.2.3   The best practicable environmental option

The best practicable environmental option approach is based on the view that once wastes have been produced, the environmental costs of all disposal options must be assessed before one medium, such as the sea, rather than another, such as the land, is chosen. Air, water and land options should be considered together, not separately, when solutions have to be found for the ultimate disposal of contaminants. The aim is to choose for disposal the least damaging option with the minimal overall environmental and human health impacts, taking into account relevant political, social, economic and legal circumstances.

5.2.4   Precautionary environmental protection

The idea that prevention is better than cure and that releases should be prevented even before evidence of damage, has been propounded for many years. This concept was developed in the Federal Republic of Germany as the anticipatory protection, or precautionary, principle ('Vorsorgeprinzip'). It was introduced internationally at the First International Conference on the Protection of the North Sea in 1984 and it was accepted at the Second Conference, in 1987, as a principle for the implementation of environmental legislation concerning the protection of the North Sea ecosystem.

The precautionary principle argues that every effort should be made to relieve the potential burdens on the environment resulting from the input of foreign substances. It is part of a policy of risk prevention aiming to reduce progressively the emission levels of all substances introduced by man into the atmosphere, water and soil. On the basis of this principle, rigorous control of contaminants was applied by the Federal Republic of Germany in certain areas, despite the lack of evidence that environmental deterioration was linked to releases, rather than to other factors, such as natural changes.

Anticipatory environmental protection, as it is evolving, raises an essential issue: are the actions for the protection of the environment, taken on the basis of our present knowledge, sufficient, or do we have to assume that the future holds risks which are beyond our knowledge and therefore need to be taken into account in our current pollution prevention strategies?

5.3   Practical Aspects of Pollution Prevention and Reduction

Practical steps can be taken to prevent or reduce pollution at several stages in its potential generation. Ideally, life-cycle strategies should be developed for the control of products by tracking them from initial production to final disposal or destruction, and this audit is done occasionally for individual new chemicals. At the planning stage of factory development, new mining operations and other mineral exploitation, and at the design stage of shipbuilding and commercial product manufacture, there should be an awareness of the range of possible problems which would interfere with the manufacture of an 'environment friendly' product. At the planning stage also, operational safety should be fully considered, so that accidents which would release contaminants are reduced to a minimum, although it must be accepted that, in spite of any provisions adopted, accidents will still occur due to human error.

This environmental awareness should be carried through to the production and operational phases, with the application of existing methodologies, where they exist, or the development of new ones, to prevent wastes arising or to minimize their quantity. Recycling or elimination of wastes by the use of alternative production processes should be employed wherever possible. Means to deal with accidents should be worked out in advance, and suitable equipment for dilution, detoxification and clean up should be at hand. In the case of oil and chemical spills, guidance should also be available on whether and when to pick up, clean up or leave to disperse and degrade naturally.

Finally, where wastes do arise and disposal is necessary, the options in each environmental sector – land, atmosphere, fresh water and the sea – must be fully explored. If sea disposal is selected, again the various options should be examined – pipeline, dumping or incineration – and the possibilities of pre-treatment of the waste should be considered, as well as the actual disposal methodology – the placing of outfalls, the fitting of diffusers, the selection of dumping grounds and the method of release.

5.4   Economic Considerations

The importance of economic considerations in relation to pollution is widely recognized and it is clear that the reduction of pollution is not cheap. The benefits to society from activities leading to pollution are often negated by the costs to the environment or society imposed by pollution, and these costs are often hidden. Since the cost of achieving complete prevention of pollution ('zero discharge') will generally exceed the perceived benefits, then some level of pollution is often accepted as a reasonable compromise. However, it is difficult to compare benefits and costs on an objective quantitative basis, even when there is knowledge of the extent, severity and time scale of impacts of human activities. Further, the balance accepted by society differs among nations, regions and interests.

Ideally, the aim would be for a universal catalogue of costs of potential pollutants, and for an inventory of all pollution-generating activities as well as of the value of the benefits derived from them. However, there are only estimates of some costs in some circumstances, and somewhat subjective views of the benefits. The long-term, widespread effects in the marine environment are not always evident, and this has led to the still not uncommon practice of using it as a 'free' service with no defined limit to its capacity to accept wastes.

To limit that practice, incentives for reduce pollution inputs or improvements in pollution control can be applied through many schemes – such as taxes, fines, permits or subsidies. However, these can be administratively unwieldy. Alternatively, a specific technique of pollution abatement may be prescribed, with the objective of conforming to emission standards. This policy, however, may be too rigid or inappropriate in some cases, and thus costly in relation to expected benefits.

The economic analysis of marine pollution problems is still in its infancy. The cost of damage to health and resources from episodic events is difficult to estimate, although progress has been made in, for instance, working out compensation for certain oil spills such as that of the *Amoco Cadiz*. While crude estimates for some corrective measures have been obtained, the assessment of the costs of continued pollution is even more difficult. Thus, the cost of the work to achieve recovery and protection of the Po river basin, which is responsible for the major part of the pollution load of the Adriatic Sea, has been estimated at over US$ 2 billion during a 4-year period. Crude estimates have also been made for the cost of constructing sewage treatment and disposal facilities for the 132 million inhabitants of the Mediterranean coastal settlements that lack such facilities; these amount to approximately US$ 18 billion or about US$ 150 *per capita*. The figures would need substantial increase to cover the costs of providing the sewerage without which treatment and disposal would not be possible.

These are among the few instances of cost estimates available. Given the magnitude of the sums involved, better estimates based on sound economics are needed. These should not only make it possible to evaluate direct costs, as in the two cases above, or to award compensation, as in the case of accidents, they should also provide the basis for deriving equitable systems of incentives, taxation and disincentives that may play a part in ensuring that pollution of the sea is kept within acceptable limits.

5.5 Evolution of International Controls of Marine Pollution

5.5.1 Introduction

A very rough estimate of the relative contribution of all potential pollutants from various human activities entering the sea is shown in Table 5.1. These figures clearly demonstrate that marine pollution is derived mainly from land-based sources and the atmosphere. The impacts from these two sources are very different. Atmospheric input to the sea is normally dilute and diffuse, while land-based inputs are often from point sources and can have long residence times in waters which are relatively enclosed by either geographic or hydrographic structure. The relative contributions from each source are different in different sea areas, as these contributions depend on the degree of industrialization, the density of populations, the extent of offshore activities and on other factors.

Although it had long been recognized that shipping operations

Table 5.1 Estimate of the contribution of potential marine pollutants

Source	All potential pollutants (% contribution)
Offshore production	1
Maritime transportation	12
Dumping	10
Run-off and land-based discharges	44
Atmosphere	33

and dumping of wastes at sea were minor (22%) sources of marine pollution, it has not yet been possible, on a global scale, to develop rules, standards and procedures for the prevention and control of marine pollution from the major sources. Indeed, major public concern between 1950 and the early 1970s focussed on cases where marine pollution had been caused by accidental oil spillages at sea and by the operational discharge of tank residues from ships. The increased practice of dumping wastes at sea, in particular into the North Sea, from the expanding chemical industry in Europe in those years likewise resulted in concern that the capacity of the oceans to receive wastes might be strained. As a result, a number of multilateral conventions for the control of pollution from sea-borne sources were adopted at that time, whereas land-based sources were considered at a later stage.

These conventions attempt to control the releases of substances to the sea on the basis of the hazards they pose to the environment and to human health. The International Convention for the Prevention of Pollution from Ships, 1973, and the Protocol of 1978 related thereto (MARPOL 73/78), in its regulations for the prevention of pollution by oil (MARPOL 73/78, Annex I) refer to a list of oils appended to the regulations. With regard to the control of pollution by noxious liquid substances in bulk, the Convention (MARPOL 73/78, Annex II) relies on several lists of chemicals transported at sea which have been allocated to different pollution categories (and therefore are subject to different legal requirements) based on their hazardous properties. A long-standing GESAMP working group sponsored by IMO and UNEP classifies annually the chemicals carried by ships in terms of bioaccumulation and tainting, damage to living resources, hazard to human health by oral intake, skin and eye contact or inhalation and reduction of amenity. These hazard profiles are used by IMO in determining carriage requirements for noxious liquid substances.

The dumping conventions categorize substances into 'black' and 'grey' lists. Black list substances are those which are either simultaneously toxic, persistent and bioaccumulated or, while essentially non-toxic, are persistent and float or remain suspended in the water where they may interfere with legitimate uses of the sea. These substances are controlled stringently and cannot be dumped in the sea in anything other than trace quantities. Grey list substances exhibit some but not all of the hazardous characteristics of those in the black list, and may be disposed of in the marine environment with special care.

5.5.2 The Law of the Sea

In 1982, the United Nations Convention on the Law of the Sea was adopted. Its provisions on the protection and preservation of the marine environment established an overall framework of governing principles and general obligations – notably those requiring states to take all necessary measures to prevent, reduce and control marine pollution from any source, and to co-operate, on global and regional bases, as appropriate, in the formulation and elaboration of international rules, standards and recommended practices and procedures and in the establishment of appropriate scientific criteria for these purposes. The obligation to co-operate also extends to the notification of imminent or actual damage, the adoption of contingency plans against pollution and the carrying out of research programmes.

The Convention lays down the basic jurisdictional regime for the adoption and enforcement of laws and regulations. For pollution from ships, global rules and standards must be applied. For ocean dumping and for marine pollution via the atmosphere, states are urged to establish and apply both global and regional rules. For sea-bed activities (within national jurisdiction), states are required to adopt laws and regulations no less effective than international rules and standards, and urged to harmonize their policies at the appropriate regional level. For land-based sources, states are required to take account of internationally agreed rules and standards, and are again urged to harmonize policies at the appropriate regional level. For the sea-bed beyond national jurisdiction the requisite rules and standards will be established by the future International Sea-Bed Authority. At the same time, the Convention provides for a wide range of enforcement measures in all marine areas within the sovereignty and jurisdiction of coastal states and beyond national jurisdiction.

5.5.3   Control of sea-borne sources

The International Convention for the Prevention of Pollution of the Sea by Oil, London, 1954, as amended in 1962, 1969 and 1971 (the OILPOL Convention), specifically dealt with the prevention of marine pollution caused by the discharge to the sea of oil residues from ships. This Convention was superseded by the International Convention for the Prevention of Pollution from Ships, 1973, as modified by the Protocol of 1978 relating thereto (MARPOL 73/78), which provides not only for a control system for operational discharges of oil from ships (Annex I), but also covers discharges from ships of noxious liquid substances carried in bulk (Annex II); harmful substances carried in packaged form, containers and portable tanks (Annex III); sewage (Annex IV) and garbage (Annex V).

In addition, it was realized in the early 1970s that the dumping from ships of wastes and other matter (i.e. the deliberate disposal at sea of wastes loaded for that purpose, as well as the disposal at sea of dredged material), was a relatively easy source to control. Accordingly, the 1972 UN Conference on the Human Environment proposed the development of the Convention on the Prevention of Marine Pollution by Dumping of Wastes and Other Matter. This Convention (the LDC) was adopted in 1972. At the same time, with virtually the same provisions, the regional Convention for the Prevention of Marine Pollution by Dumping from Ships and Aircraft, Oslo 1972 (the Oslo Convention) which covers the North East Atlantic, including the North Sea, was adopted.

The establishment of the United Nations Environment Programme (UNEP) in 1972 led to increased activities in the protection of other regional sea areas through the development of regional action plans, its first major regional activities being centred on the Mediterranean Sea. The Regional Seas Programme of UNEP expanded to cover 12 regions by 1989.

With regard to the prevention and control of marine pollution from waste disposal at sea, besides the globally applicable LDC, the following regional sea areas are covered by legal instruments:

- the North East Atlantic (including the North Sea), by the Oslo Convention, 1972;
- the Baltic Sea, by the Helsinki Convention, 1974;
- the Mediterranean Sea, by the Barcelona Protocol, 1976;
- the South Pacific Region, by the Noumea Convention, 1986.

Thus, apart from the North East Atlantic and the Baltic Sea (both administered by the relevant Commissions), only two regional seas in the UNEP Regional Seas Programme are protected by dumping protocols: the Mediterranean and the South Pacific. This is certainly because the LDC is considered adequate for controlling and regulating waste disposal in the various regions. However, it should be noted that the LDC itself draws attention to the need for states with common interests in protecting the marine environment in a given geographical area to enter regional agreements consistent with global conventions, but also to take particular account of the characteristic features of the area.

5.5.4 Control of land-based sources

Action has been taken to control the input of substances from land in only a small number of regions. The Convention for the Prevention of Marine Pollution from Land-Based Sources, 1974 (Paris Convention) covering the North East Atlantic, including the North Sea, and the Convention on the Protection of the Marine Environment of the Baltic Sea Area, 1974 (Helsinki Convention) both cover the control of substances entering their respective sea areas from land. Only two of UNEP's eight Regional Seas Conventions have been supplemented by protocols on the prevention and control of marine pollution from these sources. These are the Athens Protocol (1980) to the Barcelona Convention and the Quito Protocol (1981) to the Lima Convention.

The reluctance to develop and adopt legally binding instruments on the prevention and control of marine pollution from land-based sources can be understood in the light of the expected costs they would impose on industries, municipalities and agriculture of the prospective parties, since tight control measures, standards, surveillance and monitoring systems would have to be established. This is also the reason why the establishment of a globally applicable and all-embracing convention on the protection of the marine environment from land-based sources of pollution seems unlikely, taking into account the many different stages of development in the various regions of the world.

All international instruments on the prevention and control of marine pollution from land-based sources take basically the same approach as the LDC (and other dumping agreements): releases are controlled on the basis of two lists with different requirements, one more stringent than the other. However, as the conventions for the prevention of marine pollution from land-based sources deal mainly with indirect discharges to the sea, a complete banning of all discharges of substances on a 'black list' would be impossible. The Paris and Helsinki Conventions are laying increasing emphasis on the control of nutrient inputs which are not included in these lists.

The programmes and measures set out in the conventions give the individual contracting parties the opportunity to fix standards governing the quality of the environment and standards for discharges. The majority of the parties to the Paris Convention favour a policy of elimination of pollution by imposing strict limits on discharges through the adoption of UESs, but some feel that the best way of preserving and improving the quality of the marine environment is by fixing EQOs.

Recognizing that legally binding instruments are needed for the prevention and control of marine pollution from land, UNEP prepared guidelines that countries should take into account when developing national strategies and control mechanisms and bilateral, regional and multilateral agreements (Montreal Guidelines, 1985).

The Montreal Guidelines recommend that states should develop, adopt and implement comprehensive programmes and measures for the prevention, reduction and control of pollution from land-based sources. Once the desired present, medium- and long-term uses have been identified, and the associated objectives set for a water body, a number of control strategies may be employed. These should take into account, as criteria for establishing black and grey lists, the characteristics of the substances involved and their potential to harm marine ecosystems and to interfere with the uses of the sea. They should also allow for the environmental capacity of the water bodies to which they apply, as well as for differences in regional socio-economic conditions.

5.5.5   Control of atmospheric sources

Atmospheric sources have been comparatively neglected. Provision for their control in the Baltic Sea area are contained in the Helsinki Convention. Initial measures for the protection of the North East Atlantic, including the North Sea area, from atmospheric contamination also have been taken within the framework of the Paris Convention. The lack of internationally agreed protection measures within other regions reflects the implications these would have for industry, particularly in less-developed countries. However, knowledge of their relative contribution makes it timely to consider extending controls to wider areas.

5.5.6 Effectiveness of control and prevention measures

It is difficult to assess how effective the OILPOL 54 and MARPOL 73/78 Conventions have been in reducing marine pollution by oil, but it has been estimated that without the application of these regulatory measures as much as 8 to 10 million tonnes of oil would enter the sea directly each year as a result of pumping out oil-contaminated tank-cleaning or ballast water. The amount of oil entering the sea due to maritime accidents has also fallen greatly in recent years thanks to the development of improved safety standards, navigational aids, training and watchkeeping and traffic separation schemes.

On dumping, there has been a gradual decrease in the amounts of industrial wastes and sewage sludge dumped at sea since the entry into force of the LDC.

Regarding land-based sources, very few areas are covered by relevant regional instruments and it is therefore difficult to make any meaningful evaluation of effectiveness.

In many cases the introduction of the control measures set out in conventions involves costs, sometimes considerable. For example, many of the provisions of MARPOL 73/78 have had substantial financial implications for the shipping and for administrations and industries involved in reception facilities at ports.

Assuming that the measures are well designed and appropriate to the environmental objectives and to the marine area in question, then their effectiveness will depend on the extent to which they are applied. Official initiatives such as the Governmental International Conference on the Protection of the North Sea, as well as pressure from the environmental interest groups, promote attitudes favourable to environmental protection and contribute to tighter control.

5.6 Conclusions

The behaviour of every individual contributes to the nature and extent of environmental damage. In meeting the objectives of pollution control, a high level of environmental awareness in the public is crucial. This can be achieved by provision of relevant information and by the establishment of educational programmes.

The national agencies concerned should make research results and scientific reports, as well as data bases, available to the public, and explain them clearly.

Close co-operation with business interests is also necessary. Industry is well placed to know the technical possibilities for reducing and avoiding wastes and limiting the introduction of foreign substances into the environment. Its commitment to environmental protection, supported as necessary by governments through economic means such as tax incentives, investment aid and penalties, would encourage activities consistent with the health of the environment.

Substances introduced into the environment cross national borders in water and air and, if persistent, can spread worldwide. Therefore national measures alone are not sufficient to control them. International co-operation is needed to adopt and implement uniform measures for the prevention and control of pollution. It is the responsibility of industrialized countries to assist others in achieving these common goals. Such co-operation is being developed through the international conventions referred to above.

At this stage it is not possible to identify any single overall principle which, on a regulatory basis, would guide all actions to control and prevent marine pollution. Each of the many approaches used has advantages and disadvantages and, as appropriate, each should be applied within a comprehensive framework. This would cover all sources of marine pollution, the distribution and fate of substances in the sea, and include proper hazard assessment, aiming to protect equally all compartments of the environment. It is important to recall that the paramount objective of an environmental policy should be the protection of human life and well-being, which in turn depends on a healthy environment.

Decisions, both nationally and internationally, on measures to achieve that objective are necessarily taken at government level on political grounds but must be based on sound scientific advice. International organizations, by promoting the adoption of legislation monitoring compliance with it, can provide the initiative, consistency and continuity that national authorities cannot always ensure.

Chapter 6

Overview

Broad generalizations about the state of the oceans are inevitably misleading because of their wide extent, the diversity and variability of ecosystems, the range of uses to which the seas are put, and the heterogeneity and uneven distribution in space and time of the human activities which affect the marine environment. However, in discussing those activities and their consequences, a clear distinction can be made between coastal zones and semi-enclosed seas on the one hand, and the open oceans on the other.

6.1 Coastal Zones and Shelf Seas

Man's marine-related activities tend to be focussed in shallow water near the coast, and the major source of contaminants to the sea is the continental land mass. The impact of man along the edges of the ocean is therefore unambiguous, and in places substantial degradation of the environment is evident.

6.1.1 Coastal and hinterland development

The coastal strip, encompassing the shallow-water and intertidal area along with the immediately adjacent land, is clearly the most vulnerable as well as the most abused marine zone. Its sensitivity is directly tied to the diversity and intensity of the activities which take place there, and the threat to its future is related to the increasing concentration of the world population in this area. The consequences of coastal development are thus of the highest concern. They arise not only from the variety of contaminating inputs associated with great concentrations of people, commerce and industry, but also from the associated physical changes in natural habitats, especially salt marshes, sea-grass beds, coral reefs and mangrove forests. There is further pressure from the increasingly rapid development of mariculture around the world, both from direct contaminating inputs and from the intentional alteration of habitats to accommodate fish farms.

The pressures exerted directly on the coastal strip are exacerbated by activities inland. The use of rivers for waste disposal leads to consequences at the coast often far from the site of the original input, and there is a widespread need for improved treatment facilities inland, and for better control of inputs to fresh water. Also, alterations made, for a variety of reasons, to freshwater drainage systems often result in adverse changes in estuaries, for example in their sedimentation and salinity regimes. In addition, the coast is affected by other activities in the hinterland, such as intensive crop production and stock rearing as well as various land-use practices, including irrigation and large-scale forest management.

One major consequence of these activities is siltation. Increases in sediment load have important impacts *per se* in addition to those of any associated contaminants. Some coastal ecosystems, particularly those dominated by corals and submerged grasses, require clear water,and there is now indisputable evidence that deforestation inland is reducing the extent of coral reefs through increased sediment run-off from soil erosion. Sediments also reach the sea from mine tailings, from disposal of bulky wastes such as those arising from titanium dioxide production and from fossil fuel combustion, while dredged material dumping and marine mining activity result in sediment mobilization and redistribution. Even activities leading to a higher rate of nutrient input, by enhancing primary production, increase particle fall-out to the sea bed and alter the composition of benthic communities, sometimes to the point of death from anoxia. It is recommended that further attention be given to silt as a marine contaminant of considerable importance.

These activities on the coast or inland are directed towards meeting immediate needs, but in nearly all cases far-field and long-term effects are not considered or even envisaged at the planning stage. If the marine zone is to be properly protected, full account of such activities must be taken. At present many countries require environmental impact assessments before major projects are approved, but often the assessments are not sufficiently comprehensive and do not include long-range effects, such as the coastal impact of inland developments. The special need of the coastal strip for long-term protection must be generally recognized and policies developed and implemented to cover not only specific locations, but also major stretches of coasts and whole river basins aiming to control erosion and siltation, to restrict excessive nutrient input and to reduce chemical contamination.

6.1.2 Eutrophication

Rivers provide a major input of nutrients to the sea, but such materials remain largely within the shelf areas, only a small fraction of the nutrients ultimately reaching the open ocean, which remains oligotrophic. Over the past few decades increased discharges of nutrients to the coastal zone have occurred worldwide. Sources of nutrients are diverse – sewage disposal, industry, agriculture, stock rearing – and they vary from area to area. In some locations, the increases in concentrations of dissolved nitrate and phosphate, and of organic carbon, together with organic accumulations in the sediments, have brought about changes in the structure of planktonic and benthic communities, often with substantial ecological and economic consequences. There have also been increases in the number and extent of episodic events, such as exceptional plankton blooms, which alter natural ecosystems and threaten the mariculture industry and coastal amenities. Algal blooms have also been associated with some of the frequent episodes of seafood contamination by biotoxins, sometimes with very serious consequences for human health. It is seldom possible to connect with certainty unusual algal blooms to enhanced nutrient levels, and detailed studies of some recent cases have not shown convincing cause-effect relationships. There is clearly a need for a better understanding of the dynamics of phytoplankton growth in coastal waters, and it is recommended that appropriate studies be undertaken.

Considering the future, it is relevant that the current anthropogenic inputs of nutrients are at least comparable to those from natural sources, and that these inputs are related to present population densities in coastal regions and their hinterland. Within the next 20 to 30 years a near doubling in human population is projected, and even greater rates of increase are expected in some coastal areas. Such changes will inevitably be accompanied by increases in agricultural and livestock production, and by further expansion of mariculture. Thus, anthropogenic inputs could become several times greater than the natural background, and the effect on coastal waters globally could then be on the scale at present found only in enclosed areas such as the Baltic and Japan's Inland Sea.

Given that these increases occur predominantly in developing countries where waste treatment facilities are few and population growth is most rapid, and assuming that remedial measures are not taken, then a worldwide problem is to be expected. The most severe effects will be found in areas with dense and increasing population, on coasts with restricted water circulation. Such particularly sensitive locations can be identified now. A major study should be initiated by UN agencies to estimate the scale and severity of these potential global effects, and to encourage appropriate and effective action which might include radical changes in techniques for sewage disposal and in farming practices inland.

6.1.3   Sewage contamination

While the input of human sewage to the sea is a major cause of deoxygenation and eutrophication and a source of chemical contaminants, it also introduces pathogens, posing a major health risk to consumers of seafood and to recreational users of the littoral zone. The consumption of contaminated seafood is firmly linked with serious illness, including viral hepatitis and cholera. Earlier work on the connection between bathing and disease produced conflicting or ambiguous results, but epidemiological studies have now provided unequivocal evidence that swimmers in sewage-polluted sea water have a higher incidence of gastric disorders and that the increase is correlated with *Enterococcus* counts in the water.

The studies further indicate increased incidence of non-gastric disorders (ear, respiratory and skin infections), but in this case there is no correlation with indicators of sewage contamination. It is clear that current health standards are not generally adequate and often are not properly enforced. Improved control and monitoring is therefore essential. Also, because conventional treatments may not in all circumstances be the best or most economic approaches for dealing with sewage, consideration should be given to all options – land disposal, offshore discharge or dumping, incineration and even deep-sea disposal should be evaluated.

6.1.4   Plastic and other litter

The increasing use of synthetic materials to replace glass or tin for containers and natural fibres for ropes and nets has introduced a new type of marine pollution. These materials are not readily degradable and they persist in the environment. Being buoyant, they float in the sea. Plastic straps and rings used for packaging entangle marine mammals, fish and birds, while discarded fishing nets continue to trap marine organisms for long periods. Persistent plastics accumulate in shallow water and strand on beaches. Recent reports of hospital wastes washing up on shorelines with possible risks to health are also of concern.

While some of these problems are alleviated by 'good housekeeping', they are best tackled at source. Extensive regulations already exist at the local level, and legislation to prevent disposal of plastics is now being introduced in several countries as well as internationally. The quality of the coastline and the safety of marine organisms could be much improved by greater public awareness and involvement, and by more rigorous enforcement of existing rules.

6.1.5 Chemical pollutants

In recent years, advances in analytical techniques, sampling procedures and quality control have led to overall improvements in the reliability and accuracy of environmental data, and today measurements of chemicals at low concentrations in marine samples can be made with an assurance not possible even a decade ago. The main chemical contaminants are those synthetic organic compounds that can build up to relatively high concentrations in enclosed seas and in coastal and estuarine waters receiving inputs from rivers, as well as more directly via pipelines and dumping operations. Only in exceptional cases has it been demonstrated that elevated concentrations of arsenic, cadmium, mercury and lead in coastal waters have adverse effects on human health and on marine organisms.

For synthetic organic substances the effects vary greatly from compound to compound. TBT degrades relatively quickly in the environment but its continued use will perpetuate its presence in coastal waters at levels which, though low in absolute terms, will be toxic to some marine invertebrates. On the other hand, persistent halogenated hydrocarbons have little effect on lower organisms in the sea, but they are a demonstrated hazard to top predators which accumulate residues in fatty tissues. The problem is most evident where contamination has built up over decades in the environment, such as in sediments in enclosed areas like the Baltic and the Wadden Sea, where the reproductive capacity of marine mammals and birds has been affected. Organochlorine residues accumulated in seafood can reach levels unacceptable for marketability, and the sale of some fish species has been restricted, for example in parts of the eastern USA.

As a result of public concern, the manufacture and/or use of some organochlorines is banned or restricted in a number of countries. Consequently, downward trends in concentrations in sea water and in the tissues of organisms are now being recorded in some parts of the northern hemisphere, but sediments are still a major reservoir for substances like PCBs, which may be reintroduced into biological cycles when the sea bed is disturbed. This will be a potential hazard for the foreseeable future. In some parts of the world, the use of persistent pesticides is still high, for example in countries with large cotton production.

Every year hundreds of new chemicals are introduced to the market, many of them with accompanying impurities such as chlorinated dioxins and dibenzofurans, while known chemicals are turned to new purposes. The unforeseen dangers of new materials or formulations are exemplified by TBT. Only when its effect on non-target organisms was discovered was its use seen to be unacceptable and action initiated to control and replace it. Some other chemicals, such as dichlorvos, an organophosphorus compound now used by fish farmers, are new contaminants in the sea and are causing concern. These chemicals, which aim at a selected target or are used in a limited location, are more easily controlled than others such as pesticides extensively applied on land. However, once a pesticide or an industrial compound is found to be environmentally dangerous and is withdrawn, it is inevitably replaced by another which may cause its own, perhaps less well-known, problems. The fate and effect of chemicals introduced into the marine environment should be kept under close and continued review by a suitable international body or programme.

6.1.6 Oil

Except in the immediate vicinity of sources or at the site of major oil spills, oil in the sea is generally found at concentrations too low to pose a threat to marine organisms. However, oil slicks are a significant threat to diving birds, and residual tar continues to be a serious amenity problem on beaches, affecting the economy of many communities which depend on tourism.

6.1.7 Radioactivity

Radioactivity causes public concern, but radiation doses from artificial radioactive substances in the oceans remain extremely low, and therefore do not add significantly to the radiation background of marine organisms or man, except in a few localities where exposure may be of the same order of magnitude as that from the average natural background. However, of all contaminating discharges, radioactive effluents from peaceful uses of nuclear energy are probably those most rigorously controlled and monitored. Major nuclear accidents have resulted in contamination of agricultural and freshwater foodstuffs and of seafood. Following the Chernobyl accident there was widespread contamination throughout Europe but, because the source was located inland, exposure of people through consumption of seafood was negligible and there is no reason to believe that marine living resources were affected.

6.1.8 Exploitation of marine resources

Apart from infrequent major accidents, exploitation of oil and gas resources offshore has so far posed environmental problems only within a few kilometres of installations. International agreements on environmentally acceptable ways to cope with these problems would be useful in a field where strong economic competition provides a temptation to neglect the long-term consequences of activities in the surrounding marine environment. Oil from shipping is a greater problem, but current international agreements have already contributed to a reduction in oil releases from this source. However, stricter enforcement, along with provision of guidelines, is desirable, while contingency planning and preparedness are essential to guard against the consequences of emergencies.

Exploitation of other minerals in the sea has measurable impact on the environment but this is likely to be limited to the site and the duration of the operation and can be reduced by careful planning and attention to operational procedures. There is an immediate need to establish criteria and standards for these procedures, where necessary enforced by regulations, and for standardization of the sampling, analyses and reporting of environmental information, so that similar data can be used in different geographic or temporal contexts. Such data are required before the commencement of, during and after the completion of mineral recovery operations, so as to forecast and assess impacts and to judge the success of control measures.

For thousands of years man has made use of the sea's living resources. Advancing techniques for fishing now threaten favoured species of fish and whales to the extent that most fish stocks are under pressure and some whale species have little capacity for survival. In addition, fishing activities in themselves have adverse effects on the marine environment and on a variety of marine processes and activities both in coastal areas and in the open ocean. The sea bed can be stirred up and its nature changed, damaging the habitat and its flora and fauna; food webs can be altered by fishing and by mariculture; changed genetic structures of populations may result from overfishing, from breeding practices and from the introduction of exotic species; intensive farming programmes can pollute the environment, spread pests and diseases and reduce general amenity. Pollution from fish farming can be controlled, but the spread of pests and diseases is a more serious risk since it can endanger the livelihood of many fish farmers and can have more extensive and less controllable impact on commercial fisheries when wild stocks are affected.

6.2   The Open Ocean

The main contaminating inputs to coastal regions are river-borne. They settle out mostly in the estuaries and shallow waters, and little reaches beyond the edge of the continental shelf. In the open ocean, in contrast, the two principal sources of contaminants are shipping and the atmosphere. In addition, contaminants are contributed directly to the deep sea by abyssal tectonic activity.

The shipping inputs arise mainly from operational activities and from deliberate discharges. Oil is the most obvious contaminant, but biocides from antifouling paints leach into the water along shipping routes, and recently the accumulation of ship-related plastic debris has been increasing. Dumping and accidents also contribute, but much less so than in shelf waters.

While some of the atmospheric contribution consists of substances picked up from the sea surface and later returned to it, certain contaminants are carried by air masses from the continents. These include large amounts of desert sand and materials from volcanic activity and forest and grassland fires, as well as contaminants reaching the air from evaporation, incineration and combustion processes. There is an observable decrease in concentrations of these atmospheric contaminants as measurements are made at increasing distances from continental sources.

Contamination does occur in the open oceans. Uptake of mercury by long-lived fish species justifies control measures to limit human dietary intake, but most of the mercury is derived from natural sources. Another metal, lead, shows elevated ocean-water concentrations resulting from human activities, but in some areas levels are now falling with the declining use of lead in fuels. In general, metals are present at such low levels in ocean water that they are not a demonstrated hazard to marine organisms. Synthetic organic compounds are also detectable but, again, levels are too low for effects to be expected. The study of nutrient flux to the oceans shows that present anthropogenic inputs do not have any impact beyond the edge of the shelf. Oil from shipping is detectable at the surface of the open sea but mainly in the form of degraded residues, with little impact on marine life, and the reduction in oil-related traffic, combined with tighter international regulations, has reduced the extent of this problem.

At present, exploitation of minerals and energy in the open ocean is negligible, and only a major expansion of effort would justify concern. This may seem a far-off prospect, but developments are sensitive to commodity and energy prices, which may change quickly, so complacency is not justified. Any impact from deep-ocean mining would be most likely on the sea bed. At present our understanding of abyssal ecology is insufficient to provide a reliable assessment of the effects of disturbance and sedimentation.

We conclude that in the open ocean, in contrast to coastal zones, impact from man's direct activity is slight and, while concentrations of some contaminants are enhanced, they are still low, and measurable effects are not detected. However, lead, chlorinated hydrocarbons and artificial radionuclides are present everywhere in the oceans and, given the extent of natural variability and the low levels of contamination, their effects, if any, will be observed or predicted only when there is an adequate baseline of reliable data and a better knowledge of the deep-sea processes that control them.

While it is not suggested that the massive effort required to mount extensive programmes of open-ocean monitoring would be justified at present, it is recommended that, to detect future trends, the baseline be strengthened by focussing on a small number of monitoring sites. Over a sufficient period, this baseline will also be useful in developing oceanic mass balances.

6.3 Longer-term Problems

Much of our concern is with effects that are relatively well understood and which, although sometimes common to many areas, can often be related directly to site-specific situations, for example, construction projects on the coast, disposal of wastes at sea, or the operation of fish farms. There is, however, the possibility that low levels of contaminants could build up insidiously in the sea with subtle effects causing damage to wide areas in the long term. Because of the difficulty of recognizing changes of this kind against the background of natural variability, they can be studied only indirectly through a combination of experimental approaches (both in the laboratory and in mesocosms), field surveys and modelling of process dynamics. Support for an intensification of such work is recommended.

Other long-term and truly global concerns are the impacts of human activity on climate and the ozone layer, and their consequences for the marine environment. These issues raise questions about causal agents and mechanisms, effects and geographical extent and expected time scales.

Changes in the ozone layer, which may result in increased fluxes of ultra-violet radiation and possible harmful effects on marine life, are attributed largely to chlorofluorocarbons in the atmosphere. The recent adoption of the Montreal Protocol to the Vienna Convention has shown that international agreement can be reached and anticipatory action taken.

Although the effects on marine ecosystems and resources of climate changes resulting from the increase of greenhouse gases in the atmosphere cannot at this stage be predicted with any confidence, they have become a matter of growing concern. The rise in sea level associated with these changes is an alarming possibility for populations living in low-lying lands. Action to avert or delay man-induced climate changes will have to be taken on the continents, involving shifts in fuel consumption patterns and energy policy and alterations of agricultural and land-use practices.

Such issues are for the most part relevant to medium- or long-term time scales, in contrast to most of those discussed so far, which are short term, affecting us now and requiring action immediately. In preparing this review, it was decided to focus on the short-term problems but, in reacting to them, to be aware of the others and to take them into consideration as and when sufficient understanding develops from current research.

6.4   Prevention and Control

Many activities have adverse impacts on the sea, and public awareness of the degradation of the environment is increasing, with strong attitudes emerging in favour of its protection. A concept attracting increasing support is the precautionary principle which, in its original formulation, was carefully integrated as part of a national package of approaches to environmental management. This principle proposes action even in situations where damage has not been demonstrated, in order to safeguard against possible future risks. However, especially for waste disposal, it is essential to take a balanced view after consideration of all the options, including the banning of waste-producing activities. It must be recognized that prevention of pollution in one sector of the environment could transfer it to another where the consequences could be more severe or less predictable.

Thus, in comparing the relative advantages of land or sea disposal, the possibilities and implications of, for example, contaminating ground water with sewage must be weighed against the expected impact of disposal to the marine environment. Reviewing the options involves more than just selecting the appropriate environmental sector to receive the wastes – atmosphere, land, fresh water or the sea; there are also issues of storage or destruction; containment or dispersion; use of accessible or remote sites. In the longer term, improved waste management, with emphasis on waste reduction, will make a significant contribution to the prevention of pollution in all sectors of the environment. Obviously, cost considerations must also be relevant in reaching decisions, and an economic assessment should be part of any process leading to them.

It is important for example to see how the costs of damage relate to the costs of action to minimize or avoid pollution. Advances have been made in the techniques for analysis of costs incurred as a result of marine pollution and in the evaluation of the benefits of control and abatement. Inevitably, however, the values attributed to a potentially polluting activity and the cost of preventing or cleaning up after it must reflect local conditions and values.

In addition, the difference in approaches and languages of natural sciences and economics may lead to misunderstandings or even to misguided decisions. Initiatives are therefore needed to improve communication and understanding, so that both disciplines can be directed to the common aim of safeguarding the marine environment.

Protection of the oceans involves control of many human activities. The legal framework, both national and international, for protection of the marine environment is critical. Internationally, oil pollution was the initial concern because it is the most visible and has been for a long time the most objectionable form of pollution. For this reason legislation was enacted early to control it.

More recently, dumping at sea and pollution from land-based sources by chemicals and litter and, increasingly, by nutrients have become the subject of regulation. Land-based sources are indeed the main contributors to marine pollution of all kinds but their control involves hard and costly decisions. To be effective, it will require major changes in long-established agricultural and industrial practices, as well as the development or expansion of waste treatment facilities both along the coast and far inland, sometimes well beyond the boundaries of the coastal states concerned. So far, only four marine conventions contain provisions for the control of land-based sources. More should include such provisions, particularly in regions where little national legislation regulates land-based pollution.

Pollution from the atmosphere is also significant, and its control is even more difficult. As yet few steps have been taken at international level to achieve it, although it is only at that level that regulatory measures can be effective. It is important that existing regulations be extended and strengthened but it is equally important to enforce legislation.

However, pollution *per se* is not the only threat to the oceans. Runaway coastal development is as damaging to habitats and marine resources. Coastal development is subject to regulation in some countries, but often the authority is fragmented among poorly co-ordinated administration units. No international agreements or guidelines on coastal development are available, and this gap should be remedied well before most areas are built up, mangroves cut down, swamps and lagoons reclaimed and coral reefs destroyed.

Appendix A

Working Group on the State of the Marine Environment

The Working Group was established by GESAMP to undertake the review of the state of the marine environment and to prepare this report.

Members

J.M. Broadus
Woods Hole Oceanography
   Institution
Woods Hole
Massachusetts 02543
United States of America

E.D. Goldberg
Scripps Institution of
   Oceanography
University of California
La Jolla
California 92093
United States of America

E.D. Gomez
Marine Science Institute
University of the Philippines
UPPO Box 1
Diliman, Quezon City 3004
Philippines

G.D. Howells
Department of Applied Biology
University of Cambridge
Pembroke Street
Cambridge CB2 3DX
United Kingdom

A. Jernelöv
IVL
Box 21060
S – 10031 Stockholm
Sweden

P.S. Liss
School of Environmental
   Sciences
University of East Anglia
Norwich NR4 7TJ
United Kingdom

A.D. McIntyre (Chairman)
Department of Zoology
University of Aberdeen
Tillydrone Avenue
Aberdeen AB9 2TN
Scotland, UK

G. Needler
Institute of Oceanographic
   Sciences
Deacon Laboratory
Wormley, Godalming
Surrey GU8 5UB
United Kingdom

A. Salo
Finnish Centre for Radiation
    and Nuclear Safety
PO Box 268
SF – 00101 Helsinki
Finland

H. Shuval
Division of Environmental
    Sciences
School of Applied Science and
    Technology
The Hebrew University of
    Jerulsalem
Jerusalem
Israel

J.H. Steele
Woods Hole Oceanographic
    Institution
Woods Hole
Massachussetts 02543
United States of America

P. Tortell
Department of Conversion
59 Boulcott Street
PO Box 10-420
Wellington
New Zealand

A.V. Tsyban
Natural Environment and
    Climate Monitoring
    Laboratory
State Committee for
    Hydrometeorology
Pavlik Morozov per. 12
Moscow 123 376
Union of the Soviet Socialist
    Republics

H. Windom
Skidaway Institute of
    Oceanography
Savannah
Georgia 31416
United States of America

Associated Experts

R. Arnaudo
Office of Ocean and Polar
    Affairs
Department of State
Washington
DC 20520
United States of America

M.J. Cruickshank
Marine Minerals Technology
    Center
University of Hawaii
811 Olomehani Street
Honolulu 96814
Hawaii
United States of America

S.W. Fowler
International Laboratory of
    Marine Radioactivity
2, Av. Prince Héréditaire Albert
MC – 98000 Monaco
Principality of Monaco

Y. Halim
Department of Oceanography
University of Alexandria
Alexandria
Egypt

J.B. Pearce
Northeast Fisheries Center
NMFS/NOAA
Woods Hole
Massachussetts 02543
United States of America

L. Magos
Medical Research Council
  Laboratories
Woodmansterne Road
Carshalton
Surrey SM5 4EF
United Kingdom

Technical Secretary

F. Sella
United Nations Environment
  Programme
Palais des Nations
1211 Geneva 10
Switzerland

Appendix B

Group of Experts on the Scientific Aspects of Marine Pollution

GESAMP is an advisory body consisting of specialized experts nominated by the Sponsoring Agencies (IMO, FAO, UNESCO, WMO, WHO, IAEA, UN, UNEP). Its principal task is to provide scientific advice on marine pollution problems to the Sponsoring Agencies and to the Intergovernmental Oceanographic Commission (IOC)

Members

J.M. Bewers
Marine Chemistry Division
Bedford Institute of
   Oceanography
POB 1006
Dartmouth
Nova Scotia
Canada B2Y 4A2

J. Blanton
Skidaway Institute of
   Oceanography
POB 13687
Savannah
Georgia 31416
United States of America

R. Boelens
Irish Science and Technology
   Agency
Shannon Water Laboratory
Shannon Town Centre
Shannon
Co Clare
Ireland

J.M. Broadus
Marine Policy Center
Woods Hole Oceanographic
   Institution
Woods Hole
Massachussetts 02543
United States of America

D. Calamari
Institute of Agricultural
   Entomology
University of Milan
Via Celoria 2
20133 Milano
Italy

H. Chansang
Phuket Marine Biological
   Centre
PO Box 60
Phuket 83000
Thailand

R. Duce
Graduate School of
   Oceanography
University of Rhode Island
South Ferry Road
Narragsansett
Rhode Island 02882
United States of America

W. Ernst
Alfred-Wegener Institut für
   Polar und Meeresforschung
Colombusstrasse, 2850
Bremerhaven
Germany

J. Gray
University of Oslo
Institute of Biology
Department of Marine Zoology
   and Chemistry
PO Box 1064
0316 Blindern, Oslo 3
Norway

G.D. Howells
Department of Applied Biology
University of Cambridge
Pembroke Street
Cambridge CB2 3DX
United Kingdom

C. Ibe
Division Physical and Chemical
   Oceanography Nigerian
   Institute for Oceanography
   and Marine Research
PMB 12729 Victoria Island
Lagos
Nigeria

A. Kapauan
Department of Chemistry
Ateneo de Manila University

PO Box 154
Manila
Philippines

J.M. Lopez
Center for Energy and
   Environment Research
University of Puerto Rico
College Station
Mayaguez
Puerto Rico 00708

A.D. McIntyre
Department of Zoology
University of Aberdeen
Tillydrone Avenue
Aberdeen AB9 2TN
Scotland
United Kingdom

J. Pernetta
Department of Biology
University of Papua New
   Guinea
Box 320 UNI PO
NCD
Papua New Guinea

J.E. Portmann
Ministry of Agriculture,
   Fisheries and Food
Fisheries Laboratory
Remembrance Avenue
Burnham-on-Crouch
Essex CM0 8HA
United Kingdom

A. Salo
Surveillance Department
Finnish Centre for Radiation
   and Nuclear Safety
PO Box 268, SF – 00101 Helsinki
Finland

H. Shuval
Division of Environmental
   Sciences
School of Applied Science and
   Technology
The Hebrew University of
   Jerusalem
Jerusalem
Israel

P. Tortell
Department of Conservation
59 Boulcott Street
PO Box 10-420
Wellington
New Zealand

A.V. Tsyban
Natural Environment and
   Climate Monitoring
   Laboratory
State Committee for
   Hydrometeorology
Pavlik Morozov per. 12
Moscow 123 376
Union of the Soviet Socialist
   Republics

P.G. Wells
Marine Environment Quality
   Conservation and Protection,
   Environment Canada
45 Alderney Drive
Dartmouth, Nova Scotia
Canada

H.L. Windom (Chairman)
Skidaway Institute of
   Oceanography
POB 13687
Savannah
Georgia 31416
United States of America

Appendix C

Annexes to the Report

I.	R. Arnaudo	The Problem of Persistent Plastics and Marine Debris in the Oceans
II.	M.J.Cruickshank	Exploitation of Non-living Marine Resources: Minerals other than Oil and Gas
III.	R.M. Engler	Disposal of Dredged Material
IV.	S.W. Fowler	Concentration of Selected Contaminants in Water, Sediments and Living Organisms
V.	E. D. Goldberg	Selected Contaminants: Tributyltin and Chlorinated Hydrocarbon Biocides
VI.	Y. Halim	Manipulations of Hydrological Cycles
VII.	International Maritime Organization*	International Conventions on the Prevention of Marine Pollution: Control Strategies
VIII.	A. Jernelöv	Recovery of Damaged Ecosystems
IX.	P.S. Liss (ed)	Land-to-ocean Transport of Contaminants: Comparison of River and Atmosphere Fluxes
X.	L. Magos	Marine Health Hazards of Anthropogenic and Natural Origin
XI.	A.D. McIntyre	Exploitation of Marine Living Resources
XII.	A.D. McIntyre	Sewage in the Sea
XIII.	J. B. Pearce	Development of Coastal Areas

*Office for the London Dumping Convention

These annexes have been published by UNEP in Regional Seas
Reports and Studies 114/1 and 114/2.

Appendix D

GESAMP Reports

The review of the health of the oceans. (1982) *Rep. Stud. GESAMP*, (15): 108 p. Published also as *UNEP Regional Seas Reports and Studies* No. 16.

Review of potentially harmful substances. Cadmium, lead and tin. (1985) *Rep. Stud. GESAMP*, (22): 114 p. Published also as *UNEP Regional Seas Reports and Studies* No. 56.

Thermal discharges in the marine environment. (1984) *Rep. Stud. GESAMP*, (24): 44 p. Published also as *UNEP Regional Seas Reports and Studies* No. 45.

Review of potentially harmful substances. Arsenic, mercury and selenium. (1986) *Rep. Stud. GESAMP*, (28): pag. var. Published also as *UNEP Regional Seas Reports and Studies* No. 92.

Land-sea boundary flux of contaminants: contributions from rivers. (1987) *Rep. Stud. GESAMP*, (32): 172 p.

Review of potentially harmful substances. Nutrients. (in press). *Rep. Stud. GESAMP*, (34).

Appendix E

Selected References

Anonymous (1988) Widespread coral bleaching in the Caribbbean, *Mar. Poll. Bull.* **19**: 50.

E. Bacci (1988) Mercury in the Mediterranean, *Mar. Poll. Bull.* **20**: 59–63

G.W. Bryan *et al.* (1987) Copper, zinc and organotin as long term factors governing the distribution of organisms in the Fal Estuary in southwest England, *Estuaries* **10**: 208–21.

D.F. Boesch and N.N. Rabalais (eds) (1987) *Long Term Environmental Effects of Offshore Oil and Gas Development*, Elsevier, London and New York.

B. Bratbak (1988) Cleaning up the sea bed – the Norwegian approach, Oljedirektoratet (ISBN 82-7257-260-5).

COST 47 (1985) *Coastal Benthic Ecology: 1979–1984*, CED Env. Res. Prog., Science, Research and Development Directorate, Brussels.

E. Goldberg (1982) *The Health of the Oceans*, The UNESCO Press (ISBN 92-3-101356-4).

M. Holdgate (1979) *Environmental Pollution*, Cambridge University Press, Cambridge.

R. Johnson (ed.) (1976) *Marine Pollution*, Academic Press, London.

R. Marchetti and A. Rinaldi (1989) Le condizioni del Mare Adriatico. In: Melandri (ed.) *Ambiente Italia*, ISEDI, Torino.

T.H. Pearson and R. Rosenberg (1978) Macrobenthos succession in relation to organic enrichment and pollution in the marine environment, *Ocean. Mar. Biol. Ann. Rev.* **16**: 229–311.

D.J.H. Phillips (1988) Selenium in the San Francisco Estuary: an opportunity, *Mar. Poll. Bull.* **19**: 191–2.

L.O. Reiersen *et al.* (1988) Monitoring in the vicinity of oil and gas platforms: results from the Norwegian sector of the North Sea and recommended methods for forthcoming surveillance, Int. Conf. on Drilling Wastes, Calgary, Canada.

L. Reutergardh (1988) *Identification and distribution of chlorinated organic pollutants in the environment*, SVN Rep, 3465, Solna, Sweden.

A.J. Southward (1980) The Western English Channel – an inconstant ecosystem, *Nature* **285**: 361–6.

The World Commission on Environment and Development (1987) *Our Common Future*, Oxford University Press.

UNITED KINGDOM (1987) *Quality Status of the North Sea*, Department of Environment, London.

G. Weaver (1984) PCB contamination in and around New Bedford, Mass., *Environ. Sci. Technol* **18**: 22a–27a.

Index